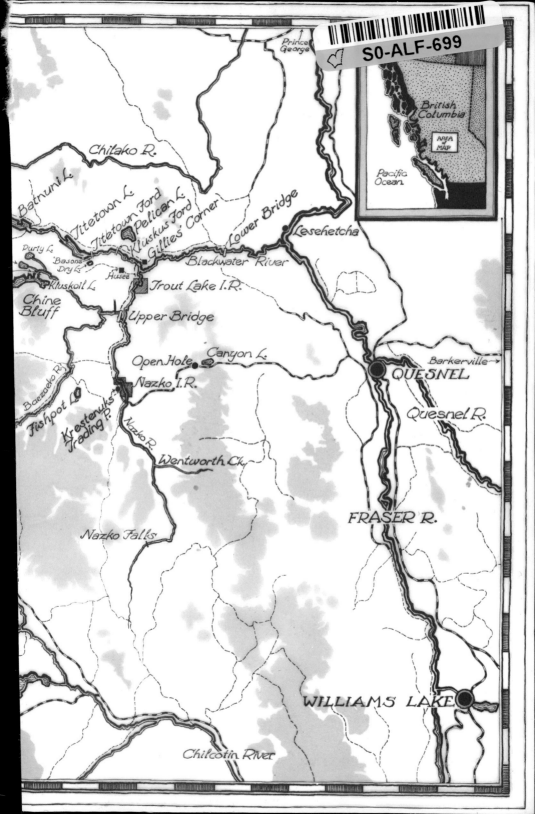

Prince
George

British
Columbia

AREA
OF
MAP

Pacific
Ocean

Chilako R.

Batnuni L.

Titetown L.

Titetown Ford

Pelican L.

Kluskus Ford

Gillies' Corner

Lower Bridge

Lesehetcha

Purty L.

Basons
Dry L.

Husee

Blackwater River

Kluskoil L.

Trout Lake I.R.

Chine
Bluff

Upper Bridge

OpenHole

Canyon L.

Barkerville →

Baezaeko R.

Nazko I.R.

QUESNEL

Fishpot L.

Krestenuks
Trading P.

Quesnel R.

Nazko R.

Wentworth Ck.

Nazko Falls

FRASER R.

WILLIAMS LAKE

Chilcotin River

Blackwater River

Bill Hellin

Blackwater River TOA-THAL-KAS

William Hillen

McClelland and Stewart Limited/Toronto/Montreal

The Canadian Publishers
McClelland and Stewart Limited
25 Hollinger Road, Toronto 374

Printed and bound in Canada

*To Momma Jessie,
my first fishing partner*

Contents

Truly, to my best discernemente, it seemeth good sport and honest to see the fair, bright, shining fishes deceived by crafty means and drawn out upon the land.

Juliana Berners, *The Boke of St. Alban's,* 1496

While strange creepy creatures came out of their dens, And watched them with wondering eyes.

Lewis Carroll, *"The Hunting of the Snark"*

Chapter
One

The Call

". . . the best way to explain it is to do it."
Alice's Adventures in Wonderland
Lewis Carroll

The first subtle impulse came from across the restless Fraser. The northwesterly squall rattled the chains on the office windows and, glancing out, I saw bluebirds from the mountains and prematurely tinted birches. An early autumn–September had crept silently upon us.

Also, the morning had passed with few distractions, and the incubation baskets were reasonably clear of the previous hatch. If kept in captivity for ten days, office correspondence frequently answers itself. It was past twelve noon when the secretary from next door entered, complained of the cold, wriggled into her sweater, and demanded that I return her coffee and conversation. I happened to mention that I could think of a number of places I would rather be, mainly on a fishing trip.

"What's with this fishing? You arrive back dirty, beardy, half-starved and with a few little fish, and claim you've had a nice time."

Personally I cannot think of a better way to loaf creatively—pleasant phrase that implies doing what you want when you want. Fishing is conducive to concentration and provides an escape from everyday turmoil; it means associating with the wildlife community, an opportunity to take a look at their social relationships.

Then Joe Spehar gusted in and I knew I was lost. I was surprised to see him because he should have been putting up hay on his spread out near Nazko. But he had come to town for grub: "I've got half the rancheree working on Big Meadow. They can sure eat!" His old Buick had run dry just out of town, and he was walking. We went out to lunch.

Joe is a Yugoslav, and an old-timer to the country who staked out his ranch in the Blackwater wilderness in 1912. Now ninety years old, he says his father made it to a hundred and nine: "I gotta long time yet." Watching him hop into a saddle, I think he has. Joe disappears for days on end, and tells no one where he goes. His main hideout remains a secret to me, but I have reason to believe he has more than one.

Joe can tell bear stories and when telling them his ice-blue eyes take on a wild look, his grizzled beard bristles, and his head weaves from side to side like a surveying silver-tip. As he becomes older and smaller, he becomes fiercer and fiercer.

He knows how I love to fish. I usually prefer to fish alone, but always tempt him to come along with a few well-chosen phrases to arouse his interest. If I profess ignorance about some facet of the sport, or how to fish a certain pool, then he has to show me and he's a dead duck no matter how many strays have to be rounded up or how much hay has to be stacked.

I have always been interested in fishing of any kind, but the conditions of my growing-up years turned me into a fly fisherman. Vancouver, where I was raised, was on the sea, but I was attracted early to the countryside which had
2 many trout and steelhead streams comparatively un-

affected then by pollution, metropolitan claims, and heavy fishing demands. I was fortunate because my family maintained a cottage on nearby Seymour River. It was a simple cottage by present day standards but considered ample at that time, and we kids kept it occupied all summer between times of doing a lot of camping and fishing on our own. At fourteen I teamed up with the three skookum Lamont brothers and we built our own log-and-cedar shake cabin. We hunted grouse with slingshots, a pursuit I've not yet completely outgrown, and we were truly bloodthirsty. We started packing heavy rifles when fourteen and shot coyotes and deer, and ducks and pheasants in season or out. We did not shoot each other, and we did not turn to drink, and we did not hang around girl-watching corners. And of course we tried to poach all game.

Conservation officers usually know that nearly every boy is a natural poacher, and after catching a young offender they like to sit down and talk to him. A boy wants to find out things for himself and sometimes his actions are rather odd, at least to the adult mind. Small boys, for example, like to fool around small creeks to fish for or merely to look at small fish, to use tackle of their own manufacture, and to lay across logs and study the aquatic life. All more important than fish-catching. If introduced to the outdoors by an adult who makes reasonably certain the boy does not drown, the youngster will gradually develop a lifelong interest and it won't be long before he'll be wielding a fly rod with the best. But a boy has to want to do these things.

All the time I was growing up I had an insatiable curiosity about fish. I could identify Dolly Varden and sea-run cutthroat trout, but no one explained to my satisfaction the life habits of steelhead. I caught my first one, a twelve-pounder, when I was ten. I had captured plenty of six-or-seven-inch trout which went back to the stream unharmed unless grub was short, but didn't know whether these little fish were young steelheads, cutthroat, or salmon. Nor did many of the adults with whom I was acquainted; at that time fishermen were and may still be, very ignorant about fish. The tiddlers were, of course, 3 mostly second-year steelhead, as I realized by the time I was fourteen.

Occasionally I met an angler who knew fish and equipment, and one such explained to me at an early age the fundamentals of fly-fishing. Certainly my equipment wasn't much but I caught fish and got along with what I had. I remember when I invested eight dollars in a double-taper line! I have never enjoyed fishing the streams and lakes with hardware since. Each to his own, but somehow I think I appreciate fly-fishing more than fishing with spinning gear.

Old Joe too is pretty well a fly-fisherman, but of a different type. He uses live "bugs," and is a master at knowing how and where to find the ones he thinks should be best at the time. This is a nature lesson in itself. His favorite is the stone or "salmon fly": "You catchem in the willows along the river. Put them in a snoose box—snoose makes bugs perk up." His fishing pole is just that, a fifteen-foot willow with twenty or so feet of line, but he uses different rigs. I've found Old Joe poles all over the Blackwater basin. By their cut you can always tell them: he gouges a ring around the butt in which to store some line. I asked him once what happens when he hooks a big fish and has only a few feet of line to play it. "Have a good strong pole, a good strong line, a big hook, and just flippem out. Your hooks are too small!" In fact, I have watched him hang several large trout, line and all, in a tree behind him. Joe has fished his favorite fishing holes this way for fifty years, and the method is good enough for him still. I admire his simplicity.

Like Joe, I am a watcher of fish. One spring day when, as a boy, I was prowling the other side of the Seymour, I discovered a new stream. Exploring up its gurgle I found it fed from a timbered flat, from the tangled roots of fir, cedar, maple, alder, and tall hemlock. It was quiet and dark in there. I came to a small gravelly pool and, wonder of wonders, in it were two steelhead. I crept through the ferns and skunk cabbages to the very edge, until I could peer through the water shadows to watch those two big fish, an arm's length away, gently finning and working their gills in a graceful side-to-side sallying. The fish-pole was completely forgotten. I watched them for hours

4

that day, and again on days following. Certain that the fish were aware of me but ignoring me, I became part of their ritual. One small, spellbound boy, strangely delighted, didn't seem to bother them all all. One day they were gone; one day they returned through the torrents and canyons and rocks to the sea. The small world of the pool seemed empty but I knew that the spawn lay buried under the clean white patches of gravel on the gold-colored bottom, and I wondered when the eggs would stir. I sat watching as though I could do something to help while the trickle flowed on.

Naturally I asked Joe if he had been out on the Blackwater lately. He hadn't. What with haying and with whiteface cows getting into more trouble than enough, with their getting stuck in swamps, and calving too late, he'd been too busy. Only yesterday an Indian had ridden into the ranch and told him that one mootase (a range cow), had been bogged down in a swamp. The Indian had roped it and pulled it out with his saddle horse and Joe had given him a box of bullets.

"But," Joe said mysteriously, "she'd be good at Chinee Falls right now." And added slowly, eyes becoming vacant, "Lotsa big ones. I caught two of the biggest up there. In winter."

"Steelheads?" I asked.

"Steelhead? I don't know that kind. Are they trout? I know those real big red-meated ones that travel in pairs aren't around much in summer. It's too cold to fish in winter, unless you get fish-hungry. The Indians catch them sometimes. Minnie, that old Indian woman from Trout Lake rancheree, she understands all about them. She says there used to be thousands. When she was a little girl all the Indians caught them in the winter. Then that big slide the railway blew into Fraser Canyon, just after I came to the country, buggered things up."

I felt something like an itch coming on. I ordered Joe another beer: "How's the fishing right now?"

"Good fishing right now. That's what I've been telling you," he replied patiently. "All the way down Chinee Falls. All the way right from Kluskoil Lake the whole two miles down the length of the falls."

As it happened I'd always been in too much of a hurry to try the falls when passing Kluskoil. The last time by, when returning from the Dean River country, I had chosen the northern route and was making tracks for Dry Lake. A pack horse had been giving nothing but trouble – never did a horse travel so far with hobbles on in one short night. Even if he did not stray, each morning I'd have to hunt him like a moose because he would hide and stand so still that his bell would not ring. I finally turned him loose to find his own way home.

I had drifted the Blackwater several times from Joe's place near the upper Blackwater bridge to the Euchiniko River: with all the bends and some paddling through widenings of the river, a fairly long day, a distance of about thirty miles. I asked Joe if he knew of anyone who had ever taken a canoe down the Blackwater from Kluskoil to the upper bridge. He said that the old Indians occasionally used the river when they were beaver trapping, but no one had done so for years. He thought it practical, however, for he had ridden along the banks and it looked okay to him.

A twinkle came to his eyes: "She'd sure be a fishing trip!"

"If you go to Chinee Falls and I'm not around when you pass," he continued, "just make yourself at home. I gotta batch of sauerkraut and stuff working in the cellar."

After driving Joe to his old car, I felt a certain compulsion to visit Slim Campbell, who was working with his bulldozer at Bouchie Lake, six miles west of town. Three o'clock in the afternoon was too late in the day to start more work anyway.

Slim was working across a field. "Figured you'd be along soon. How about a cold one?"

We drove to the boat landing where he had his beer cooling in the lake. A bittern, like some hidden boatman working a dilapidated hand pump ker-thumpety-thump, called along the shoreline. A medley of grebe calls flooded over the lake – handsome Holboells and graceful, slender-necked Westerns. Amid the outlandish clatter echoing from all around the lake came the quack of a hen mallard, and 6 a loon called once.

"Can you get away for a few days at Chinee Falls?" I asked.
"Sure. When do we leave?"
"Early tomorrow morning?"

Our plan was to drive to Nazko and have one of the Indians, probably Little Charlie Cremo, take our outfit in by wagon over Poplar Mountain trail. Since this trail was less travelled than the one to Kluskus, we'd include a power saw for any downfall blocking the way. We'd fish the Chinee Falls area and then drift downstream to the upper Blackwater bridge. The sixteen-foot aluminum canoe would be best.

Back at the office I wrote some post-dated letters to give the impression that I was still around, and enclosed them with a note to the secretary next door explaining when to mail them. I left behind me a slightly guilty conscience and in the typewriter a half-finished letter dated five days later.

Sadsack had been waiting patiently in the station wagon most of this time. Now he sensed something brewing, and licked my ear to tell me that whatever it was he was for it.

Because
of Cats

"Are you—are you fond—of—of dogs?"
Alice's Adventures in Wonderland
Lewis Carroll

Sadsack was a professional cougar hound. Being a cougar hound might seem to be a glamorous profession, but his life was mostly work, even though he was on the government payroll as one of the highest paid dogs in the province – twenty cents a day.

For fifty dollars I had been given my choice of the litter and had chosen the biggest one, chestnut and white, not too evenly marked, but a pup with oversize feet, a broad back, good haunches, and good chest. When he waddled out of the heap, squatted in front of me, and looked up with his sad, enquiring gaze, I had the feeling he had chosen me. After a start on pablum and eggs and milk, and then on home-cooked meals and rare beef and cannery reject sockeye salmon, he developed into a strong 9

From a distance I examined Kelly's ears, his broad skull and powerful jaws; his blue-black coat, deep chest, and broad back and haunches; his dewclaws, his toenails, his track in the spring slush. I examined a guard hair from his fur coat and compared it with ones from wolves. And his smell. Somebody was spoofing Frank, or Frank was spoofing me, or Kelly was spoofing the whole town. If there was doggie ancestry in his makeup it didn't show.

Loner Kelly took a liking to Sack. When in town, he called each morning, accepted a tin of sockeye and took Sack on a tour, introducing him to the finer things to be found around town, teaching him patience and how to con a housewife out of a free meal: Don't ever step on the tulips. Hook the screen door with your nose, gently, and let it bang. Then stand back and look hungry. Lick your chops lightly to get the idea across, and give them a look of protective adoration like they're the only woman alive.

Occasionally Kelly would come to the house during the evening and stay for the night. Sometime toward morning, usually about four, he would slip into the bedroom, his eyes glowing in the pale light, and I would awaken more from his presence than from the cold nose pressed against my arm. I'd get up and let him out, and without a backward glance he'd lope over the fence and be gone, as silent as a ghost.

Once when Sadsack and I were camped somewhere along the headwaters of Deacon Creek, in the Quesnel River basin, who should arrive but Kelly. The previous day a cougar which couldn't or wouldn't tree had clawed Sack and only through luck had I managed to get him back in. This was a four-dog cougar, really a snare or trap proposition.

I had examined several of his deer kills. Instead of plucking the hair from a deer carcass like most cougars, this puss peeled off the hide. He was on his kills in two leaps and was proficient. He was also taking more game than his share. He had caught a free-loading silver fox right at one of the kills—usually permissible—and the fox had not had a chance. A coyote at another kill hadn't made ten feet. In a cave, he had dispatched a porcupine almost as neatly as would a fisher; normal, except he had

not eaten it. On this visit he also annihilated a family of
packrats. He had killed two moose as easily as he killed
deer, but did not eat them either. This oddball was clearly
possessed by more than mood. He seemed to hate anything alive.

In the few days we had trailed him around we had
learned considerable about his habits, and the territory.
His leaving a distorted, pigeontoed track with his near
hind foot caused me to wonder about what else might be
askew: very strange, too, was the absence of the tracks of
other cougars, fresh or old, male or female. Deer were so
numerous it was normal for Sack and I to jump over fifty
in a day's travel, so other cougars should be around. No
one else hunted this range and there had been a number
of cougar the month before. This puss, with the largest
track I had ever seen, was interesting but abnormal, and I
did not want him in the country.

I was worried about Sack, for if a cougar decides to
make a stand on the ground a dog really has no chance.
Cats go into high immediately and are unbelievably fast
for a short distance, but because of a narrow chest cavity
and small lung capacity they have no stamina for a long
chase. When cornered, this one would regain his wind and
kill Sack as quick as a wink, or more likely ambush him.

Sack was willing but had met his match. Kelly could
not have arrived more opportunely. If we could only catch
the puss at the right time: tired out; stomach plugged with
deer which was pressing against his narrow chest. If the dogs
could only hold the cougar at bay until I arrived on the
scene. If I could only hold Kelly long enough in reserve.
We'd be smart to pack up and go home. Instead, I set to
work preparing to hold Kelly with a sleeping pill: roasts,
stew, tenderloin. I coaxed him and fed him until he looked
ready to burst, but I held back a roast in case he became
hungry during the night.

I awoke at six. Kelly was still with us. Day broke on a
very cold world; about forty below zero. No breath of
wind: the blue smoke from the birch fire pillared to a
polished blue sky as I fried thick slices of deer liver to
split three ways. Fifteen hundred feet below, icy fog stirred
over the Quesnel River and denser patches billowed above 13

the unfrozen rapids. No creature moved save the black-capped chickadees who were cheerful visitors to our camp as they came searching for handouts. Amazingly, their toothpick legs did not freeze and snap off in the cold. Seven moose still browsed or bedded down on a flat, a half a mile away. They had moved only a few hundred yards in the past week. Three cows were large in calf and I wondered, having examined their range, how they got enough to eat.

I loaded a small hunting pack with essentials, checked that the action of the rifle was slick as silk, and the knife razor sharp, and the snowshoe rigging perfect. We started out. Kelly seemed to be getting the idea, but kept stepping on the heels of my snowshoes. We slipped along four or five miles. Perfect snowshoeing: four feet of snow, a good crust, six inches of powder. Sack could walk on top; Kelly broke through occasionally. The tom would wallow once off a deer trail.

We cut across his fresh trail and followed it. He had killed another deer, eaten a huge meal the night before, slept, and eaten again this morning. So far, perfect. He was heading north into a steep broken country and to save a lot of tracking through difficult terrain, we climbed northwest to the highest ridge, then swung east along it and watched for his track. We met it at noon coming up from below and minutes old.

We followed. The hunters were restless. I silenced them and watched each track for signs of the cat having heard us. Cats, for animals, appear to have poor scent faculties, but keen sight and hearing.

He saw us, circled a rock pinnacle, and ran. The opportune moment for us to act. I passed the word to Sack and Kelly and ran after them as fast as I could go on snowshoes. Sack's bugle roared through the valley. Kelly uttered a long howl and finally barked. Sack changed note; he was in trouble and was now screaming. The cat was cornered. I couldn't go fast enough down a steep canyon, and struggle up the other side.

In a little draw I was suddenly on top of life-and-death action. The dogs had the cat pinned up a sloping broken-off snag. Sack had run up it and I saw him get swatted

14

off. Kelly was lunging and slashing from below while
blood spattered the surrounding whiteness. Tail snapping,
eyes blazing, the cat was fully occupied and seeing me
didn't improve his temper. He was looking for a place to
leap. My rifle was plugged with snow but I took the risk
and pulled the sights down on his left ear. The 6.5 Mannlicher kicked like a mule and the cougar never heard the
shot echo through the canyons.

Suddenly it was bitter cold. Blood congealed fast. I
built a fire and boiled a pot of tea while the other two
had their revenge. What a gory sight! When those furies
were expended, quenched, and they were cooling in the
snow, I skinned the cat. They would live meanwhile.

This cougar not only had a crooked foot but had at
least twelve inches missing from his tail, enough to upset
his balance for the fine art of tree climbing. Perhaps
frozen off when a kitten, or chewed off in a fight with
another cougar. His ears were nubbins chewed down from
love-making and fighting. He had an old wound on his
shoulder, a deep scar down his belly, and his eyes were
still puffed from a recent encounter. His foot had been
badly smashed, maybe by a faulty bear trap, and undoubtedly caused him pain. Although this accident had
not, as yet, affected his ability to obtain food, it was a
misfortune for any animal, especially a cougar.

I took needle and sutures and iodine from my pack and
sewed up Sack. My science was not the neatest and he was
in rough shape with numerous head and ear slices; gums
and teeth grinning through a slice in his chops; a bubble
forming over a small hole in the back of his skull. I plas-
tered on a bandage and as usual he did not complain. I'd
get him to Doc as soon as possible.

"All right, Kelly, you're next." Kelly was not too sure.
Neither was I. A nasty cut gaping and still leaking ran as
neat as a knife-slice from elbow to dewclaw. I thinned a
bottle of dettol with tea and told him that cougar claw
wounds are the most infectious cuts he'd ever get, and
while talking I poured the disinfectant down the slice. He
licked the frost off my buffalo-fur cap as I clamped and
stitched. His hide was tough, my hands cold; I dared not
look into his eyes. "Kelly, it's not perfect, but the best I

can do." Without thinking I ran my hand along his back, the first time I had ever really touched him. He licked the blood, dettol and all, off my hands.

I boiled another pot of tea, dumped in sweetened milk, and we split it before taking a short-cut trail to our camp where we toasted ourselves around a leaping, roaring fire high above the river. We grilled deer tenderloin and roasted ribs and cracked for marrow. Desert-close stars came out. A silver moon. Aurora Borealis streamed and mounted its changing arc. The trees snapped shots into the clear cold silence. My demons slept like the dead.

Sadsack and I left for home in the morning, happy if we never saw another cougar. Kelly had left during the night, but with his jagged silver streak down one leg of his blue-black coat he continued to visit us occasionally in town. Then he disappeared. With a forty dollar bounty on wolves, he didn't have much chance.

Sack's education was becoming complete. By this time too he was Old Sack to the kids in town who took him rabbit hunting. I took him after birds and he became a fair retriever. One time I sent him into a patch of woods for a bobcat but he returned in a few minutes, a stupid look on his face, carrying a fat Canada goose and limping something terrible. Obviously she had attacked him but he brought her to me without a feather ruffled. After we liberated her, he went in and treed the bobcat.

One morning I received a call from a small community schoolmarm. A cougar had followed some children on their way to school and the little French teacher and her class were frightened. *Sacre!* The worst time of the year— spring. Not a gentle, balmy, well-settled spring, and not a really advanced spring, but the early, undecided spring of Central British Columbia: a few warm days and frost-free nights; snowmelt starting to run from exposed mountain slopes and trickling into valley arteries; the beginning, misty-lime blush of budding willow and aspen; vanguards of Canada geese and whistling swans coning their way northward, as retreating snowline and icebound ponds sur- render; the emerging grizzlies seeking bulbs and roots on awakening mountain slides, where brave spring flowers 16 and lilies burst and blossom amid winter-left havoc and

icy seeps; fishing gear being fondled and sorted in readi-
ness for the first open lake and wild, ice-released trout;
anxious cruising loons, unable to wait, staking out re-
served territory. The first run-off. A time when temperature can fall to ten degrees at night, a time when it can
snow up a storm, but when the strengthening, freshening
sun never fails.

I had flown over this area and found it straight on end;
broken with steep canyons and treacherous slides and rotten rock, the bottom country a jungle. Frost-heaved rock
ready to roll, water running, little hope for tracking-snow.
But the schoolmarm sounded nice. I took extra care in
packing and slipped in fifty feet of nylon rope, some de-
hydrated food, and crampons for the icy slopes.

The schoolmarm was brave, and had placed a bucket
over one of the tracks. We told her it most certainly was a
cougar, a large tom. I checked a few likely looking places
nearby and talked with some neighbors. This rugged valley was a place a person usually waited for cougars to
come out of, but we were going to have to go in.

We started at daybreak. I dispensed with the 6.5 as
being too cumbersome and took the 32.20 pistol. Temperatures had dropped to hard freezing during the night
and the snow was a crunchy mess, but we followed the
twenty-four-hours-old track. We had no easy way.

At higher elevations, the hard-packed granular spring
snow made tracking difficult. I sent my cougar-sniffer
ahead. He cold-trailed, losing the scent and again finding
it, an occasional bugle telling all. I spotted him on a steep
arête two miles away. He the hunter, and I his support. Or
so I hoped. Suddenly his bugle echoing through the crags
indicated that he was on a fresh trail and in hot pursuit.
He soon ran out of my hearing and I could only climb to
the general area of where I had last heard him, and keep
going until dusk when I camped. I knew that my camp
was better and safer than his. This was no country to
roam after dark anyway, and I did not know where I was.

Morning dawned blustery. I tried a new direction, into
real cougar country. I found Sack's track frozen in the
melt of the previous afternoon: ice had cut his foot and
made tracking easier. About noon I thought I heard him

in the roughest imaginable broken country. Cursing the wind, I detected a thin whisper of bell swirling through the sheer walls of the canyons. He was over a divide.

I found him in the rocky jungle of a hanging valley, his voice nearly gone, and his quarry up a twisty mountain pine and none too secure. I don't know how the puss managed to climb this tree, a picturesque whitebark pine with a short, tapered trunk and a flat crown with branches like a bedspring. For safety, I tied up Sack and shot the cougar twice behind the shoulder. He died across the branch-bedspring. Sack released, I had to climb up, perch over a cliff, and force the carcass through the springs with Sack, suddenly come to life, pulling from below. The cougar perhaps had made the long leap up there to escape discovery. No doubt Sack had had him up other trees earlier.

I boiled us a pot of tea, admired the scenery, and grilled tenderloin cougar steaks for Sack who had for the first time stuck with a cat for twenty-four hours. We then slid down a snowfield to the village and gave the school-marm her cougar hide, a robust old tom with perhaps questionable motives.

Driving home the next day, I told Sack that it was almost worth putting up with his shenanigans: "You're a pretty good hound-dog."

He thumped his battered tail, almost knocking the windows out of the station wagon, danced his little front-feet stomp, and licked my ear, seeming to say that the feeling was mutual.

Chapter
Three

Nazko Country

"What sort of people live about here?"
Alice's Adventures in Wonderland
Lewis Carroll

Cariboo autumn had brought another brisk morning, splashed the green ridges around town with yellow, and laid sparkling dew on the grass. The day promised to be perfect but the clear sky was streaked with feathery wisps, Mare's tails, curved filaments ending in tufts with up-turned edges, a cirrus-type cloud usually indicating an approaching warm front and worsening weather conditions.

I loaded the pick-up: tent; sleeping-robe; binoculars; camera; prospecting pick; Hardy fish-poles; fly lines, both floaters and sinkers on Hardy reels; flies and leaders; and a char-dredging outfit with a lead-core line on a surf-casting reel. The 6.5 went along as a matter of course. Sad-sack, who was well aware of the sequence, and who had 19

probably slept in the pick-up, checked each item off with
a tail-thump. We drove to The Nugget for breakfast and
watched Wong Kee grumpily tick off the abacus. Then we
went for Slim.

In the station wagon Sack usually sat on the floor behind me and on my shoulder plopped his head. This bur-
den weighed several pounds and became so heavy after a
time that I'd shift it to the back of the seat, but it had a
way of creeping back up. Sometimes he seemed to fall
asleep, but day or night he really didn't miss a thing.
Rabbits and mice rated an eyeball flicker; moose, deer,
and coyotes, a head lift; bobcats, frenzied action. In the
pick-up, though, he would stand behind the cab with his
head pushed along the outside of it and with his ears flap-
ping in the breeze, looking like the figurehead of a ship.

Slim stowed his gear and we loaded the canoe. From
Quesnel to Nazko Indian village, or rancheree, and Paul
Krestenuk's trading post is about seventy miles. A few years
ago, getting through the mudholes was a constant battle but
in summer and fall now the road is usually good. It travels
fair moose country—burns, logging slash, swamps, pothole
lakes and meadows. This range is only fair for deer now;
much of their winter housing has disappeared because of
logging.

Several coveys of ruffed grouse and Franklin grouse, or
fool hens, were picking up their morning gravel from the
road. Mother grouse hatches a large family all on her
own, usually eight or ten. She's an interesting character in
early summer as she fakes a broken wing to lead danger
away from her chicks. Following an accident, her only
concern is for the survivors and she ends up in late summer with about five. A few white-tailed ptarmigan sometimes winter here; large flocks of willow ptarmigan some
years winter farther west, near The Mountain.

The grouse population increases steadily for about ten
years and then suddenly collapses, regardless of habitat,
nesting conditions, or hunting pressure. The collapse is so
severe that the forest seems devoid of life, and the few
survivors, hunted by predators, will be almost unap-
proachable. Since most fur-bearing animals are predators,
20 and owe their existence to the grouse and rabbits and les-

ser species, the disaster records itself on the fur-catch records. The cycle is not limited to grouse, but also includes the varying hare or snowshoe rabbit. An occasional rabbit or grouse will supplement a traveller's diet in the wilderness. For two or three years after the crash, though, this supplement will be almost impossible to obtain without a great deal of hunting. The exceedingly wary survivors form a good recovery stock. During such times of hardship some northern inhabitants, notably snowy owls, migrate south and manage to survive the winter. Most other species just seem to disappear.

The reasons for the cycle are not yet understood, but the explanation must lie in general living conditions just before the climax, although "general living conditions" are tough to analyse, because there's so much variation in the birds' habits. Sharp-tail grouse, for example, normally flock and engage in community-type activities; ruffed grouse and Franklins, on the other hand, are loners, and the family group requires plenty of elbow-room, yet all are subject to cycles. Food depletion does not matter; where there is ideal cover and food, the decline is most marked.

When the cycle is at its lowest the predators also decline. The lesser four-year cycle of mice, lemmings, shrews, and voles shows a modification on the ten-year cycle in certain other species, notably Arctic foxes and snowy owls. Because he is not a carrion eater but subsists mainly on rabbits the Canada lynx is particularly vulnerable; the curve on his chart closely follows that of the snowshoe rabbits, so called because their large hairy feet serve as snowshoes. During the "famine," lynx will take domestic birds, and even a spring lamb. Many different animals depend one upon another; thus a variety of creatures may be all but wiped out because of the cycles of their prey. Disease and parasites then take their toll.

The Nazko road climbs gradually, past Moose Springs and past Summit Meadows, to a 4,000-foot pass below The Mountain. We looked down on small Canyon Lake which drains into Puntataenkut Lake and winds up as Baker Creek in West Quesnel. At Open Hole Divide, the headwaters of Udy Creek, we start down the west slope into the Blackwater River basin. Another ten miles farther on, the road crosses the creek itself. Mudholes! I've seen grown men sit down and weep near Old Joe's ranch.

Bouncing past his gates one morning I bogged the pick-up in one of the more notorious mudholes, crawled out the window, and walked to Joe's to see if he were home. He was. With two of the biggest Percherons I've ever seen –and surely one would have done–we returned to the scene and hooked them on. My crossed fingers behind the wheel were not crossed hard enough. The horses, with Joe after them and the pick-up and me still attached, ran away through the woods and stumps where Joe had been cutting firewood. Quite a ride, and the undercarriage all but wiped out. I could straighten the bent tie-rod, but on starting the engine I had no oil pressure, and knew the Blackwater trout and the Euchiniko geese would suffer little this trip.

Joe towed the remains to his ranch, turned the team loose, and unconcernedly and casually made a pot of coffee. This everyday event had merely happened to test our skills.

"Any oil with you?" he asked inexplicably. "Gotta be sure we have enough oil. I'll see what's in the Buick."

Curses and threats came from the dark bowels of the blacksmith shop where the Buick sat. He finally emerged carrying a pail of the dirtiest looking engine oil I've ever seen, and that I said looked as though it had been in the Buick since 1926. The hole in the dark place again swallowed him. Again abusive language. He returned with a reasonably clean bedpan and a pair of lady's red panties.

"We'll strainer through these. Letter settle awhile, and strainer again."

I, naturally, took note of the approximate size of the panties. It seemed to indicate that the lady could take care of herself; yet I wasn't entirely sure that she wasn't now held prisoner in the blacksmith shop. Interesting. Maybe Joe's lonely bachelor life wasn't so lonely after all.

"You got any lead? Outside of your bullets?"

"Two bars. About 150 pounds in the tail of the pick-up for weight."

"Getter out. We'll knock off what we need."

I hadn't, at this point, the foggiest idea what we were

doing, but the oil and lead crises were apparently under control. As instructed, I crawled under the pick-up with a socket wrench and dismantled what remained of the oil-pan which Joe examined critically and carefully pounded out the dents. He disappeared along the creek bank and returned with a bucket of blue clay.

"We'll build a mould!" he proclaimed: "Getta fire going!"

The pan and clay mould positioned correctly, he very skillfully poured in molten lead and sealed the hole where the drain-plug had been.

"Bettern it was," he announced, knocking off the rough edges. I bolted up the pan, and again began thinking about geese.

"Starter up," he ordered, "and see if there's a drip."

I caught him flat-footed and suggested re-straining and pouring in the oil first. What would he use for a strainer now? Sure enough he entered the black dungeon a third time. I listened more carefully to the gruff and muffled swearing and high-pitched complaining, but couldn't understand the words. I felt sure there were two or three people. Out he came carrying another set of ladies' step-ins, of a more shapely size. I regarded Joe in a new light. He poured in the guck and the engine purred. But before going on to Dry Lake for a goose hunt and some fishing I had to clear up a question.

"Where'd you find all the ladies' panties, Joe?"

"These are ladies' pants? Guess the ladies must leave them. Always so many people coming and going through here. Can't keep tracka nothing."

Past Snaking River, a creek draining a hundred square miles of meadows and swamps to the south, Slim and I crossed Nazko River bridge and continued on another three miles, past Nazko Indian village to Paul Krestenuk's trading post where we stopped to visit and to hear the latest news on the "moccasin telegraph." Paul was born at Hocheen, near the city of Odessa on the Black Sea, in 1888. "On the wrong side of the Danube," according to Old Joe. With little more than his life he escaped from Russia in 1912, during one of the upheavals that preceded the Bolshevik Revolution, arrived in Quesnel in 1913, and settled permanently at 23

Nazko in 1920. With a few dollars and some financing he began burying fur, and branched out to Kluskus and Ulkatcho when prices were good. Paul was, in fact, responsible for settlement in times when life was far from easy.

He has built several important trails through the region and has helped keep others opened. His engineering feats are legend. I have seen him camped out on the Nazko Road for weeks with an all-Indian crew, and living under the most primitive conditions while blowing rock, filling mudholes, and laying corduroy over muskeg, the air humming all the time with man-eating mosquitoes. He can skirt a road across a shale slide or bridge a river or log-crib a mountainside so well that only a major catastrophe can demolish his work.

His store, on the other hand, is a merchandiser's nightmare. He believes in a fair profit, one per cent: buy an item for $1.00 and sell it for $2.00. Simple one per cent. Store hours Paul never heard of. I've tried to sleep in the rear of the store while he haggled half the night with a native trapper. He accepts jawbone, as credit is normally called, and receives payment when the trapper brings in furs. Involved deals in furs, horses, cattle, and hay go on for years. His bookkeeping methods would drive a tax man crazy, and when counting cash he seldom arrives at the same figure twice. He's thrown me a poke and left for parts unknown while I counted it and made his bank deposit. When questioned about this once, he simply remarked, "Honest man."

The Blackwater basin, generally, is excellent fur country. Most of the catch is beaver and other "water" fur, like otter and muskrat and mink. The Kluskus area is noted for the high quality of its dark-colored beavers, and Paul often received special orders from New York, Paris, and London. Wildlife management advanced a stride in 1926, when the government started compulsory registration of traplines, but this new development both solved and created problems. Previous to registration, trappers more or less trapped where they wished, or had a gentleman's agreement. Very little enforcement was possible because, except on private property, there were no legal boundaries. And since trappers did not have sole trapping rights, there was no incentive for a sustained-yield harvest.

24   However, once traplines were officially recorded and their

boundaries made legal, a man could not trap on Crown land
without permission from both the registered trapper and the
wildlife branch. Trappers began to practise conservation and
poachers were severely dealt with. Trappers could improve
trails and cabins and know that the time and money was well
invested, because the line belonged to them. Essentially,
boundaries were defined in block form, with a demilitarized
zone between. Occasionally the outbreak of a small war
between two white trappers became an excuse for conserva-
tionists to prowl the woods for peace talks. Most often the
disputes arose when a river instead of a height of land was a
boundary: one man was a better beaver-trapper than his
neighbor—he had *proved* himself better by catching them
all. But in general white trappers continued merrily along
with fewer problems each year. An annual renewal, a ten-
dollar annual licence, and an annual report on the number
and species of fur-bearers taken, retained the area for the sole
use of the registered owner, who now had an incentive for
sustained-yield trapping. Some trappers went into the guiding
business, and some also operated a small ranch and pros-
pected or panned for gold. A person could live off the
country and enjoy complete freedom.

On the other hand, wildlife field personnel required Job's
patience but didn't always have it, and, caught between
federal and provincial administrations, they made mistakes.
Huge blocks of land were registered in the name of one
Indian band: the most powerful in the band claimed the most
productive lines, and left the least productive to the others.
Some Indians traded away their traplines. Others continued
to trap secretly on hereditary traplines, especially when
blanket beaver averaged eighty dollars and small dark fisher
one hundred. Not infrequently, by the time an Indian got
around to registering his hereditary trapline, and not understanding white man's law too well, he found the line had
become the property of someone else. The big country was
seldom travelled by white men, especially Indian Agents, and
Indians had no champion to turn to.

Old Jerryboy, for instance, a Kluskus Indian living on
Lower Euchiniko Lakes claimed that Dale Kindred had
registered a traditional Kluskus line and had disposed of it to
the Lavoies, descendants of Jean Baptiste "Waccan" Bouc-

cher, the courier-interpreter with Simon Fraser on his trip to
the sea in 1808. Buster Lavoie had inherited the line from his
father and his uncle, but allowed Jerryboy to trap the south
end of the line, and the two men often worked the line
together because it was larger than Buster could handle
himself. This is poor justice though. Old Jerryboy was the last
of his family, but some other Kluskus Indian should now own
this line through hereditary rights.

An army of unemployed took to the woods in the 1930's,
and the remains of their shacks dot the country. These men
poached wherever they could, especially off easily picked
Indian traplines. As land was stripped of fur, the problems
increased, and white men and Indians clashed more and more
often. As a consequence, the Indian Affairs department
ensured that all Indian traplines were registered. In more
recent years, the department has purchased some white-
owned lines for Indians.

Within a few years the trapline files were a shambles.
Indians did not have to renew annually, and did not have to
record their annual catch because they required no trapping
or hunting licenses. This benevolence ultimately worked
against the Indians themselves, and against any conservation
measures that would ensure a continuing fur resource. In
addition, some Indians moved from one band to another.
Others changed their names: Alexis Long Johnny might
become Long John Alexis. To learn where an Indian was
trapping, you had to ask him or his chief. Some Indians took
advantage of what they considered their free and easy position and decimated the easy-to-trap, high-priced fur, and
then complained that their lines were unproductive. Perhaps,
over the years, they had already been trapped out. A few fur-
buyers who realized that conservation was necessary were of
great assistance, but most worked every illegal angle possible.
Bureaucracy, historic rights, and ceaseless trapping and
poaching of the breeding stock created an unmanageable
whirlpool.

By the early 1950's the market for wild furs had seriously
declined because of synthetics and ranched fur, but government assistance was increasingly generous and Indians could
exist on it: the days of work or starve were past. Eventually
Indian and white trappers all but ceased operations, and the
26 fur-bearers increased. Many native people fell away from

their natural livelihood. Although the wild fur market has remained comparatively low one can at least supplement one's income by trapping and be well paid for the time. Many of the new generation, however, have not been taught to care for raw furs, and therefore do not obtain top price for their catches. Many traplines now support a population of fur-bearers approaching the natural limitations of their habitat.

Fur-bearing animals cannot be stock-piled. If uncropped, the resource increases in a healthy manner, reaches the limitations of habitat, and finally destroys living conditions. The result is waste and worse: top-heavy population of adult animals; social disorder and strife; and smaller, less vigorous, poorer quality and fewer young produced than if the resource had been cropped annually, and perpetually forced to build. Among species most obviously affected are beaver, muskrats, and squirrels.

An understanding of normal behavior is fundamental to recognizing the abnormal. When species of wildlife are in a state of turmoil and strife, the social balance is invariably out of kilter. Most species show naturally aggressive tendencies toward their own kind during some part of the year at least, and these tendencies are much more common and more obvious in areas of dense populations. Very apparent too is an animal's dazed indifference to danger, an "I don't care" or "don't know what to do" attitude. Simply, the animals seem to have lost course.

British Columbia has a vast potential for quality furs, but fashion controls the market, and fashions change quicker than one can tell about them, as every career girl knows. Personally, my taste runs to the shimmer of a beaver coat, but should hair and dress styles change, long-haired furs like fox, coyote, wolf, lynx or skunk could well become "in." Mink is now teen-agers' fur. The mature woman wears sable, which is furrier talk for our fisher, a fierce little animal approximately three times larger than marten. Fisher kill porcupines, scarcely ever get pricked, and roam the tree-tops in search of their main prey, squirrels. Dark females, about half the size of males, are the most valuable. Marten are half again as large as mink, and in this country are usually dark brown with an orange-colored splash under their chins. Some are a handsome orange shade but with a white splash, others are silver-grey, chocolate, nearly black, or a combination of 27 these colors. Clean little animals, and tolerating no mice, marten become quite tame. I've had one move into a cabin with me or, more likely, I've moved in with him. Either way, within a few days he will join you for dinner and crawl all over you.

Nazko is a colorful place to visit in the spring, at "Priest Time." It's a holiday atmosphere. The Indians from Baezaeko, Kluskus, Ulkatcho, and many smaller reserves ride in to Paul's from all over this vast country, and the smell of raw furs fills the air. A few visitors usually arrive from Alexis Creek, Redstone, and Anahim Lake to help liven things up.

The Carriers and Chilcotins are straight-faced comedians who like to start some trick or joke going and then brag about how their superior intellect and outlook on life put a white man to the test. Those first white explorers discovered this characteristic and came through practically unscathed as the Indians passed them along from one group to another. One of the best tricks is to take fur-trader Paul at his own game. The Indians are naturally gregarious and we forget what a hard way of life most of them really have, and how little worldly wealth they possess. Each newcomer to this part of the world is tagged with an Indian name, often one to be proud of, but sometimes one that's not very complimentary. It will be honest though, and to the point, and you'll not be able to do much about it. A way of life that takes some getting used to, especially if you're from a civilized country.

My first trip in had been in early November, when sub-zero weather prevailed, but nice sunny sub-zero weather. Several falls of snow covered the Nazko road, the mudholes had frozen over and driving was fair. At Paul's white-washed log building the flag was flying and several shaggy broom-tails stood huddled at the hitch-rail. In an hour it would be dark and cold. My heater had konked out, and I stopped to give the place the once-over. Having met only moose in the past eight hours, I felt like some conversation.

I entered by the front door. A quick check through the murk showed five or six Indian bucks, a couple of squaws, and two or three nondescript cowpokes lounging around a pot-bellied stove. I had obviously interrupted something of great import, perhaps a plot against mankind. But not a face revealed what it might be. Once I'd absent-mindedly entered

the wrong door in a Colombo hospital and met similar dead
pan expressions: the naked gaze of twenty-seven W.R.N.
bottoms below a line of stretched army blankets. No one
screamed, however, and no one even told me to get out.

Paul, the master of ceremonies behind the counter, pre-
sented a round angelic countenance, but a blue-shadow hair-
cut, clipped skin-deep, made me wonder which of the Czar's
mine-gangs he had come from. A hand-knitted blue coat-
sweater hanging down to his knees was darned in a clash of
colors, and obviously had great sentimental value; a two-
notch torsion hoisted his pants half a notch, and heavy wool
underwear crept back to old crevices. A squaw giggled.
Completely oblivious to mundane distractions, Paul raised
questing grey eyes to some ethereal presence in the smoke-
filled log rafters aloft. There was respectful silence from his
cut-throat crew, the roughest I'd seen this side of Rangoon.
Every eye was on him. Now visibly sanctioned, hands in deep
pockets, he shifted the frog in his throat.

"He's monk material," I decided to myself.

"Where are y-o-u headed?" His resonant boom, like
distant cannon, was a proclamation as much as a question.

My pulse quickened; a discussion of my ultimate fate
seemed certain. I preferred to discuss my immediate goal
which was none of his or his archangel's business. I did advise
him, though, that Fred Rudin, postmaster of Nazko, wherever that might be, had invited me to his ranch, and that a
mail sack lay in my pick-up this very minute; no doubt
everybody would be glad to get his mail.

The smoke stratus hung over a thoughtful silence. The pot-
bellied stove belched on a slab of jackpine. The squaws
whispered klootch-talk, and one fingered my jacket. One of
the nondescripts was the first to speak but when the cross-
examination promised to be lengthy, I left.

"Watch you don't get stuck down that trail," he said as I
was going out the door.

"Yeah, last guy what left that way ain't come back yet,"
another added.

I finally arrived at Rudin's, four miles farther on, and
stopped overnight. I was full of moose meat and tea and
home-made bread, but I was twitchy. Twice I got out of bed
to peer at the sky. The last thing I wanted was to be snowed in
for the winter near a collection of bush-apes.

Early next morning I saw that the sky couldn't hold out much longer. I had penetrated a bleak countryside, but I'd give the Russian another whirl and sample his coffee which I had heard he served with Hudson's Bay cream. Moreover, I'd know just how saintly he was once I'd worked over his fur records.

He asked if I'd drive a Kluskus Indian to Quesnel, a man called Tom Baptiste, whose wife was in the hospital. I took my time appraising Tom before I said sure. As we finished our coffee, Tom said, "She's startin' snow on The Mountain. Big snow come. We better slope outa this place quick!"

It was nip and tuck getting over The Mountain and I knew I was driving the last vehicle to use the road that year, or for the next six months. Tom was silent most of the way. He was wearing an army battle jacket with campaign medals, and had just been released from service. The usual confusions and depressions had set in as he tried to fit back into the society he had left as a boy.

Now, some years later, Slim and I had lunch with Paul and talked of our expedition. He informed us that Jimmy Long John and a Messue Indian from Tatelkuz Lake had ridden the Chinee Falls trail a few weeks earlier, and had reported heavy downfall in the Dry Lake area, on the south part of The Desert. A windstorm had ripped across the east end of Titetown Lake and blown down the fire-killed trees, but I knew Slim's acquaintance with a power-saw, and I needed some exercise myself.

"Smart fellows, these Indians," said Paul. "They've been waiting for someone to come along and clear the trail. By tomorrow the moccasin telegraph will have reached Kluskus, and the next day Ulkatcho; then they'll use that trail just to see what kind of a job you do. They'll have a good laugh when they see how hard you worked."

Most of the Nazko Indians were putting up hay, but Paul sent an Indian boy riding to the meadow with word that Little Charlie Cremo and his services were required elsewhere. Slim and I would continue on to the upper Blackwater bridge, camp, and catch up on our fishing. Little Charlie, meanwhile, would take his team and wagon and a spare saddle horse to Husee or Chop Creek where we would meet him in the morning.

Chapter Four

Toa-Thal-Kas

"It's something very like learning geography,"
thought Alice. . . .

Through the Looking-Glass
Lewis Carroll

The highest elevation in the Blackwater River basin lies in the southwestern section of the watershed– 7,873-foot Far Mountain in the Ilgachuz Range. Second highest is 7,760-foot Mount Downton in the Itcha Range, the next range to the east and locally called "The Archies." These snow-capped ranges, extinct volcanos, present profiles all their own: the Ilgachuz are more sculptured and jagged than the Itchas (The Archies), though neither faintly resemble the more uniform and massive Rockies, and are quite distinct from the irregular and jagged Coast mountains. These mountains, in which the Blackwater heads, have rounded summits rising about 3,000 feet above the surrounding plateau, although some are very steep, and some are massive blocks with nearly flat tops and almost vertical walls; and some are 31 approached by long open slopes or constantly ascending lava ridges which at the crest might sheer off into a canyon or valley hundreds of feet below.

A 5,300-foot col (a pass or saddle on the divide between two drainage systems) runs between the two distinct dome-shaped mountain ranges. Through this divide, from Pan Creek on the north to Corkscrew Creek on the south, through "Archie's Pass" as it is called, lies the main Black-water-Anahim Lake horse trail. A tin cup and a corkscrew hang on a small blue spruce half-way through the pass for thirsty travellers to wet their whistles on the way.

Outdoor specialists say "never go alone" but I ignore this advice and camp here, in the pass, by myself. Picket the horses, collect the corkscrew and tin cup, *rouge St. Raphael,* hardtack, butter, Roquefort, my pipe, a bar of Ivory and head east to where water dribbles through the sun-warmed rocks. The swimming-hole, if the bears haven't wrecked it, is filled with barely tepid water; sometimes snow falls here in mid-summer. But I like to soak and enjoy the solitude, to relax and sense the peace and contentment, and to watch the sun slide past Mount Kappan and past the white summits to the west.

From Pan Creek another route branches southwest, along the west fork of the creek and below the northern face of Mount Scot. The trail winds westerly through the heart of the Ilgachuz and hooks up to the Dean River trail.

From near Archie's Pass, from the east fork of Corkscrew Creek, a trail of sorts heads into the heart of the Archies. The route crosses the Chilcotin River headwaters, goes to Baezaeko Flats and to the source of the Baezaeko River which it more or less follows to Fishpot Lake and into Nazko. Beef drives have taken this trail from Anahim Lake, but it is one of the longest cattle trails in North America and certainly the most mountainous.

From near Itcha Lake to Baezaeko Flats lie miles of alpine grazing country with vegetation quite different from the plateau cover generally. A species of bunch grass covers at least 150 square miles. Ever amid trickles of sparkling water jewel-like tarns and divide lakes dot the slopes and valleys, the surrounding beauties reflected in their clear mirrored surfaces, their brimming peripheries embroidered by the con-
32 flicting greens of exuberant grasses, wild flowers, and shrubs.

The sky seems bluer and the scented air sweeter. But here lowland dwellers lose the familiar scale indicators necessary for judging size and gain an exaggerated illusion of distance. The startling appearance of a monster deer or fox brings stunted trees and landscape into sudden perspective. This land is not only one of giants, but also dwarfs.

Being on the east slope of the Archies and protected from Pacific storms, the area gets little rain and most likely gets heavy Chinooks in winter. Several peculiarly marked grizzly roam this region. Moose and deer are numerous and the caribou are making a comeback. No sign of the elk or goat which possibly once roamed these alpines in numbers.

The northwestern definition of the watershed is of a different character and is even less travelled. From Basalt Lake the ill-defined height of land swings north-easterly along the Naglico Hills about nine miles north of the Blackwater, then around Tsacha Mountain to 6,075-foot Mount Davidson in the Fawnie Range. A low divide separates the Blackwater and Nechako watersheds about one mile north of upper Euchiniko Lake, and then swings northerly to 5,842-foot Kuyakuz Mountain and the Nechako Range to the headwaters of the Euchiniko River, about another twenty-five air miles farther north. Most of these mountains, or monadnocks, have rounded summits rising about 2,000 feet above the Nechako Plateau.

The Blackwater River itself rises from a tarn at the 6,400-foot level on the northern slopes of Far Mountain. On very old maps it's called Far Lake. Fed by melting snow and crystal springs, its blue water flows north for ten miles; then meanders through meadows and muskegs to the first major stream, Ulgako Creek, or in translated Carrier, "Branches Creek," which drains Eliguk—"branches like needles"—Lake, and Basalt Lake, one mile farther west. From the divide separating the Blackwater, Dean, and Nechako watersheds to the Fraser River into which the Blackwater flows is 115 air miles. As a trout swims, it's at least twice as far. Alexander Mackenzie, in July 1793, tracked up the Blackwater through unknown country toward the Pacific, up the Blackwater which he called West-Road River. Paradoxically, although this river was the earliest discovered outlet to the Pacific, it remains the least known.

The Blackwater—"Toa-thal-kas" to the Indians—appears 33

BLACKWATER black because most tributaries collect their flow from mus-
RIVER kegs and swamps imparting a dye to the water which stains
the streambed, and because in many places the riverbed is
composed of black volcanic rock. Some years, tributaries like
the Kluskus appear bright green during late August or early
September because of an algae bloom caused by a combination of conditions, but mainly by the tufted seeds of the
poplar tree being carried by the wind to the waters of Kluskus
Lakes. The algae runs suspended in Kluskus River in long
strings. But this bright green color seldom lasts for long and
does not make the water unsafe for drinking. Undoubtedly
the algae reduces the oxygen supply, but the fish are always
healthy, and some of the largest, darkest beavers in North
America live here. The water clears when boiled, when it
enters the main river, and when autumn frosts arrive.

The main valley trench lies generally north-east, northerly
trending, as are most Fraser River tributaries north of Riske
Creek. At some time in the remote past all waters north of the
ancient Riske Creek divide west of Williams Lake flowed
north and the Fraser River then flowed through the McLeod
Lake gap as a tributary to the Peace River and eventually
into the Arctic Ocean. The Chilcotin River, south of the
divide, has apparently always flowed to the Pacific.

The Blackwater flows through three major lakes located in
the center of the largest flat-lying lava region in British
Columbia. Twenty miles below Eliguk Lake the river enters
the largest body of water in the basin, twelve-mile-long
Tsacha "rim-rock" Lake. Below Tsacha is Kusyuko Falls—
"where red willows grow"—the highest on the river and on
the four-mile stretch which leads into eighteen-mile
Euchiniko Lakes. Six-mile Kluskoil Lake lies below the outlet of Euchiniko Lakes about eight miles downstream. This
series of lakes and Blackwater River widenings are not a part
of Euchiniko River, which should really have been named
Batnuni "char" River or Eltsaliko—"where blueberries are
plentiful." Local Indians use these names: Euchiniko in
Carrier means "the farthest or lowest lake down."

A river was usually known by one name until it entered a
large lake; below the discharge it usually had another name.
The Blackwater was Toa-thal-kas below Kluskoil Lake, and
34 Tee-a-ko above it. And a lake may also have two or three

names along its length. The significance of many place names
has become obscure, even to the Indians. One Chilcotin who
lives at Nazko most of the year and who speaks Carrier
fluently was unable to give the meanings of many place
names in the Nazko section of the basin.

Heading east to the Fraser the Blackwater is successively
enlarged by six major tributaries: Carnlick Creek; Kushya
River; Kluskus River; Baezaeko or black flint river with its
Coglistiko tributary; the Nazko; and the Euchiniko River.
The upper portions of most tributaries long ago eroded paths
into or through the lava layers, and run deep in trenches and
canyons, below escarpments and over cascades. Below Kluskoil Lake the river loops southeasterly around a spur of the
Nechako Plateau and then flows northerly from the Nazko
River junction to meet the Euchiniko River. From here the
black water boils through deeply incised canyons and flows
east to its discharge.

Roughly in the shape of a cross, the river basin drains
4,630 square miles. The maximum flow at discharge is
11,300 cubic feet a second; minimum 216. By comparison,
the Chilcotin's maximum is 16,800 and minimum 275. The
Quesnel River, with a drainage area only a little larger than
the Blackwater, has flows of 40,400 and 980, because precipitation in the Quesnel Highlands and Cariboo Mountains is
three to four times greater than over the Blackwater basin.

No flow records are available for the Blackwater's tributaries. Of the three main ones, the Nazko has the largest
watershed; the Baezaeko and Euchiniko are close in size,
with the former probably being the larger. From having
fallen into all three of them at various seasons, I would say
that the Baezaeko has the most constant average flow and is
coldest. The Kluskus likely rivals all three.

The most important tributary is the Nazko, a meandering
stream from the south, many miles in total length. Its watershed is sixty miles long, north and south, and is forty-five
miles wide near Wentworth Creek, at the middle. North of
this point the valley narrows to twenty miles. From here old
Indian trails branch out all over the country. From several
headwater lakes to the falls and lava beds fifteen miles downstream, this river is a continuation of narrow lakes, joined by
streams and sloughs, swamps and meadows. Rainbow trout

average one to three pounds but some lakes support larger ones. I've taken seven-pounders from Stump Lake at Nazko Rancheree near Paul's.

Since its watershed has ideal beaver habitat, and trappers haven't been overly active, some places in the region are usually well submerged. The rascals dam the trickles and laze about in pools that inundate meadows, trails, and low-lying areas, and have made the upper Nazko into an excellent waterfowl-nesting locality, and a favorite stopping place for large flocks of swans, cranes and geese, and all migratory birds. They pitch in to feed and rest. There have been more ducks in British Columbia in recent years, partly because of low prices paid for beaver, but hard-working ranchers, who are forever land and hay hungry, do not like beavers flooding the meadows.

The Euchiniko River flows through two major lakes, Batnuni, five miles long, and Titetown, four. At Batnuni, mooching between the big island and the west end during a thunderstorm, I found several char holes with fish between three and eight years old, and in three hours caught twenty ranging from three to sixteen pounds. Both lakes are now fished moderately heavily, and large char are more difficult to catch. Kokanee seem to be plentiful. The Euchiniko has one major tributary, Taiuk Creek, which enters the Euchiniko River one mile above Klunchatistli Lake, thirty-five air miles up from the Blackwater. Within a fifteen-mile radius from this junction lie more than twenty-five good trout-fishing lakes with rainbows to five pounds. I've captured ten-pounders and better, and had them towing the light float plane all over the lake. About three-quarters of a mile northwest of Klunchatistli there is a prominent landmark known as Sandy's Rock. A rider can go on horseback to the summit, about 900 feet above the valley, where he can meditate and, on a day with good visibility, let his gaze roam west, past the purple mountains to the peaks of the Coast Range.

A road of sorts skirts the north side of Euchiniko River as far as Klunchatistli Lake, and two main trails start there. One follows Taiuk Creek and winds up at Tatelkuz Lake—"sandhill crane's overnight resting place." The other skirts Hay and Lavoie Lakes and ends up at Tatuk—"noisy waters"—and Finger Lakes in the Nechako basin. Many of the trails have

deteriorated, as have many of the ancient Indian camp-
grounds, but these trails, and many others throughout the
country, should be indicated on maps if for no other reason
than to help downed airmen.

The general area of Klunchatistli is a rich Indian archae-
ological site: arrowheads, war clubs, pestles and mortars.
The site of an ancient armament-works, about one mile from
the lake, is littered with flint and obsidian. But there is no
graveyard, as there is on Finger Lakes. At the northwest end
of the lake there was once a large Carrier Indian village but
most of the band had moved or its population was dwindling
by the time Alexander Mackenzie went through. Within
three-quarters of a mile are what is left of dozens of wicki-up
or keek-willie holes. Over these depressions once stood the
winter homes of the Carrier people. The pit was twelve to
fourteen feet deep, and from twenty to thirty-five across. Rafters, butted into the ground around the pit and sloped to meet
above the center, were tied in with cross-members. This
framework was then covered with spruce bark, and earth or
sod. The entrance was near the peak of the roof and a
notched log provided a stairway for the dozen or more
inhabitants.

Klunchatistli was located at a crossroads and must have
been an important village and, even though it was not on the
main east-west artery along the Blackwater, trails led in all
directions from the village, linking it to Bella Coola and
Kimsquit on the coast. The trail from Klunchatistli to the
main road was by way of Batnuni Lake, around the western
slopes of the Poplar, or Marcel, Hills, to the Blackwater. It
skirted close to "Unnamed" or File Lake where the ancient
trail worn deep in the ground can still be traced.

It is not true either that the trails Mackenzie followed to
Bella Coola have disappeared. Though here a horse trail and
there a road, they are in many places still discernible. They
have been deeply worn, and have been kept in repair by the
Indians travelling between their hereditary lands by horse
and wagon, by fur-traders, by prospectors on their way to the
gold fields, by early settlers going to Ootsa Lake from Bella
Coola, by ranchers and occasional survey parties, and by
people who just like to explore and fish and hunt wilderness
country. The trail Mackenzie followed was a main route 37

from the interior to the coast and was kept in repair in order
that interior "brokers" could go to the coast and trade buckskin, furs and hides for oil. The coastal Indians produced an
oil from fish called eulachon and traded that oil to the
interior people who had no source of their own. This "great
road," as Mackenzie thought it, was known as the "Grease
Trail."

Each spring schools of silvery little two- to three-year-old
fish, up to twelve inches long, ascend major British Columbia
rivers and sometimes spawn several miles from the ocean.
These are eulachon. The spawn sinks to the bottom, ruptures,
and an adhesive membrane anchors each egg. The parents
die and the young descend to the sea in mid-summer, soon
after hatching.

Indians sometimes use dipnets to capture eulachons, but
oil production calls for a long, windsock-shaped net set in the
river and usually left overnight. In olden times the nets were
constructed of nettle-fiber. The little fish are dumped without
ceremony into a rectangular wooden vat. Secured by a lid,
covered lovingly with conifer boughs to shade them from the
April sun, they are left to stew in their own juice for several
days and then transferred to another vat and boiled. Ice-cold
water is then run into the immense cauldron of bubbling goo,
and the oil rising to the surface is skimmed off into containers
into which hot rocks are lowered to steam away the water.
The oil is then strained and restrained in spotless refinery
equipment to produce a pure oil with no fishy taste. You can
eat it, drink it, or wear it.

A narrow but fair gravel road leads to the upper Blackwater bridge and crosses the river fourteen miles north of
Nazko, where beef cattle grazing on ranchland improve the
valley scenery. Small lakes lying near the road feature mostly
kokanee, averaging the customary ten to eleven inches, although one once provided habitation for a seven-pound rainbow. About a mile south of the bridge a jeep trail leaves the
Nazko road and heads west for five miles to the lower
Baezaeko and to one of Old Joe's original hideouts. The
main road continues north twelve miles from the bridge to
Gillie's Corner. Just past Trout Lake Rancheree, about eight
miles along, a horse trail turns off to Husee, to Dry Lake and
38 to Poplar Mountain. A bridge crosses the Euchiniko River at

Gillie's Corner and here the road forks. East, it follows the Blackwater to the lower Blackwater bridge along what Mackenzie called "high banks." From there a good but narrow road heads north-easterly to Punchaw Lake, Naltesby Lake, and the Nechako River. South from the bridge, the way follows, more or less, the old Collins Overland Telegraph line trail past a shallow waterfowl and pelican swamp, Pantage Lake, and into Quesnel. West from Gillie's Corner, a jeep road skirts the Euchiniko River to Klunchatistli Lake. At the Pelican Lake turn-off, a jeep road continues on to Vanderhoof or Prince George. From the northeast end of Batnuni a jeep road heads north for fourteen miles to the Chilako River and joins the Tatuk Lake road to Vanderhoof.

Mackenzie required four days to travel the distance between the Fraser and Dry Lake. On the third day the party found the Grease Trail, and followed it along the high dry terrace between lower Blackwater bridge and the Euchiniko. The Indians, he said, had no covering but their beaver garments, and that of his guide was "a nest of vermin." On the second night out, though, he shared the guide's and "passed a night of sound repose" in spite of his sense of smell threatening to interrupt his rest: the guide's hair was greased with fish-oil and his body smeared with red earth. On the fourth day they crossed rolling ridgey country, drumlins and eskers, broken by glacial meltwater channels and swamps. Much of this area has poor drainage and ill-defined divides. The heavy silence is broken only by the sound of wind through the trees, the creak and groan of a leaning lodgepole, straining against its complaining neighbor, the forlorn call of a loon indicating yet another small lake, the bark of a fox, yelp of a coyote, or moan of a wolf from some elevated ground. A region Mackenzie does not describe too well, for it has little to describe but it does have some attraction for which I cannot account.

Jim Hatter and I maneuvered the first pick-up through to Klunchatistli Lake in 1947, but these roads, which were built mostly by the guides and ranchers who followed the old Indian trails, have not been improved over the years and are best travelled with four-wheel-drive rigs. The government does little or no road maintenance and has no official sign posts, and those at the strategic locations have been erected

by the game guides. There is a small store and gas pump at
Nazko River bridge. Paul, of course, used to have gas three
miles farther on at reasonable rates: one percent; wipe your
own windshield.

Slim and I arrived at the upper Blackwater bridge and
selected a camping spot for the night. At its low, early-
autumn stage, the river appeared to be ideal for fly-fishing.
We don't usually stop here, but go for more remote places
and larger trout; now we were killing time and had no better
way to do so.

Slim headed downstream to check some pools below the
Nazko, while Sadsack and I walked up the Blackwater. I'm
happy to be a simple fly-fisherman, to slip an assortment of
flies and spare leaders into a vest and set out. I rigged the
Hardy, put up a Hare's Ear for a start, and slung the binoculars over my shoulder. I fished a riffle, and released two
plump rainbows–thin iridescent band, beautifully spotted,
each about a pound and a half.

The river loops above the bridge and, following cattle and
game trails north-west for three-quarters of a mile, I crossed
the timbered flat within the loop. A lone fool hen flushed into
a spruce; the red comb above its eye proclaimed it to be a
male. I stopped to tell him how foolish he was, and he sat
cocking his head and listening. Canada jays glided from tree
to tree, sociable, murmuring softly. Black bear tracks showed
in damp sand; deer and moose tracks on the trails. At the
river a bald eagle flew from a gravel bar where he had been
feasting on a dead squawfish. The white head and tail of the
adult bird made identification simple. Until three or four
years of age bald eagles resemble golden eagles, but golden
eagles wear feathered spats; the feet and ankles of bald eagles
are bare. And golden eagles nest and hunt in more mountainous country. Both species live mostly on carrion, on dead
fish, birds, and mammals and, like the raven, quickly find
anything dead or dying.

I found a favorite reach and resumed my fishing. A cow
moose stood in the shallows; a beaver slapped the water with
his tail. I released several frisky trout weighing two and a half
pounds before the Hare's Ear became too tattered and I
changed to a Stone fly. But I noticed no difference. Stomach
contents usually show that trout take as food whatever looks

good. Occasionally however they do become selective: an Toa-
abundant hatch of some particular insect, or of young salmon Thal-
migrating downstream to the ocean. Good fishermen offer Kas
the corresponding fly and present it in a natural manner.

I had a problem of this kind many years ago in a small
brook paved with golden pebbles. Fresh from the secrets of a
deep, boulder-strewn canyon it cupped among forest giants
and moss-covered deadfalls. It chuckled out of the forest, slid
down a cut-bank, tumbled over a gravel bar and fell into the
river. The pool at the head of the run was shaded with maple
and alder and a giant red cedar. Cakes of foam lay trapped in
whirlpools and branch jungles. Two trees had fallen over it,
just right for lying on to look into the pool. It was made to the
model specified by small boys and I had trouble getting there
fast enough. Fierce black insects with pinch-stickers crept to
the bank of the pool. They dried in the sun, split out of their
skins, and hatched into dragon-flies. On first seeing the pale-
brown skin-husks along the bank, I thought that some strange
creature had sucked out their insides.

In the pool lived a family of trout, eight to ten inches long,
and with them a fifteen-inch monster. I had been trying to
catch him for two days, and had tried everything. From
under a sunken log he would inch over to my worm, nose it,
give me palpitations, and return to his cave. A smart trout.

One of the black bugs creeping up the bank would probably interest him, but getting one of those things on a hook
might injure a guy for life. Still, I grabbed one, mangled his
head from off one end and his pinch-stickers from the other,
and speared the remains on my hook. It looked good enough
to eat. Now, if I could get it past the tiddlers. I lowered it
carefully and draped it over the monster's doorway. He
darted out and grabbed it so suddenly that he almost pulled
me in. I was at "Dragon-Fly Pool," where the trout were on a
glorious binge.

Slim hadn't arrived when Sack and I returned to camp. I
prepared dinner: juicy Cariboo steaks, baked potatoes and
salad. A clatter of hoof-beats pounded across the bridge:
Zappo, Paul's top hand. He alighted for coffee.

"The mower's bust and I gotta get parts—somewhere.
Gotta big crew up there. Make hay while the sun shines." He
grinned, looking up at the sky. The cirrus was now a high,
frosted glass cover, obscuring the western half of the sky with 41

fibrous extensions advancing to the east. Zappo trotted off for Nazko.

Slim arrived. I concocted hot drinks while steaks broiled over birch embers. The river flowed quietly by, murmuring of hidden places, trout-filled lakes, and mountain passes.

"Any fish?" I asked Slim.

"About fifteen good ones. One around three pounds. They're sure scrappers."

We unrolled our sleeping bags early, and each put his head at a poplar. Geese were honking. I looked at my watch: midnight and pitch-dark. The moon shone dimly through the high, thin overcast. A goose chorus came from the mouth of the Nazko; the response came from directly overhead. Small flocks cruised past; new arrivals from remote ponds and a summer with the beaver. Young birds calling; family groups joining; choosing leaders, organizing for the long-distance flight.

Chapter Five

Calling Geese

"Fetch it home by all means —
you may serve it with greens. . . ."

"The Hunting of the Snark"
Lewis Carroll

Spring fishing is welcome, summer has its times, but autumn is best of all. September days are bright, and heavy rain unusual; nights are cool and morning mists drive like blizzards across lakes and river valleys; heavy dews quench the thirsty land. With lower air temperatures lakes start the fall turn-over; colder surface water flows from lakes to rivers, and the trout are active and prime. They run and jump farther, more often, and for longer; they seem colored in their brightest when fall leaves float on the river. In spring they may be spawning, or may have just finished. Often, too, the rivers in spring run bank-full and many pools are difficult to fish, although the lakes, especially the higher ones, give some of the best days right after break-up.

The small animals develop a noticeable urgency of be- 43

havior during autumn's progressively shorter days as they harvest for the months ahead. Night frosts touch color to the hills; snow brushes mountain tops; the cataract calls more quietly; and a stillness waits. The silhouettes of painted ridges rise like steps to purple scarps. An unsettling compulsion comes to press on the alpines, to hunt a mountain goat or timberline buck, or merely to prowl. Preparations for winter are nearly finished there, the marmots and perhaps pikas, too, already snug in their winter chambers. The golden eagle sweeps the slope; occasionally a wolverine slips by; and ptarmigan. These days may last through late October in Blackwater, and it's a time that tests a fisherman's dedication. Too often, when September has gone, I realize I neglected fishing during the finest days because I strayed again.

There are the geese, the calling geese, that make restless blood run faster. Their passing voices express freedom, intelligence, endurance, and bravery, and devotion in face of danger. They are adventure: their flight is a rendezvous with far places. The seasons could neither begin nor end without them: symbols of northern autumn thanksgiving as the rivers freeze, and springtime hope as they flow again. Watch and listen, capture momentarily the patience of geese stringing across early morning or pastel evening sky. Be stirred by wonder. The noblest of birds. Sadsack retrieved two of them from the river one early November morning when the thermometer read ten above and anchor ice was already forming. I thought he was a goner when he disappeared under a big jam below Old Joe's.

I've hunted them from the Arctic tundra to the Fortyninth Parallel, and have taken my sport from flocks of thousands. And killed the legal limit only a few times. Blackwater geese are as fine as any. Only one duck is as good eating and with a different flavor: the canvasback. But I enjoy them all, and take only what I can eat. Geese feed on duck weed and numerous seeds, tender shoots and roots, on plentiful tuberous water plants in the beaver ponds and marshes, lakes and rivers. In the rivers they feed on eel grass which they fold neatly to tuck into their crops. They nest on small safe islands on undisturbed lakes where they raise their young.

44   Many Blackwater geese do not fly the interior strip of the

Pacific flyway but migrate to and by way of the coastal inlets.
A Blackwater-raised Canada need not fly north and south
at all. (Many go no farther than the main coastal river deltas
and gravel bars and coastal muskegs, and remain there
during the coldest January and February weather.) He need,
in fact, fly no farther than 300 miles from his birthplace and
few people would ever see him. Unfortunately the coastal
wintering areas are fast being appropriated by men who are
not interested in sanctuary needs, and the pressure of their
activities is now threatening the species.

A few years ago hunters abided by an unwritten code: hunt
geese in field and marsh, but leave them be on the main
rivers. These hunters understood that harassing geese by
river-hunting them was the quickest way to hurry them
along. With no place to rest and take gravel, shot at from
long distances with rifles, pressured at every turn, they depart
and avoid this inhospitable countryside. Many of the hard-
to-kill birds are crippled. There is no sadder sight than a gut-
shot goose, wings set and gliding for miles, out of range.
Geese deserve better sportsmen, but, until they have them, all
easy-to-reach arterial rivers should be closed to waterfowl
hunting, as well as some river marshlands and deltas, in order
that birds have a place to rest undisturbed and where unor-
ganized birdwatchers can have a field day.

The Fraser River benches, with their grain fields high
above the river, have provided the goose hunts I have most
enjoyed. Prowling my look-out near Castle Rock one late
afternoon and evening I had Ed Aitken's upper barley field
cased as a good place for a morning shoot. Ed is a tidy but not
too tidy farmer—some grain is always left for the geese.
About 125 Canadas and Lesser Canadas in five flocks had
set down, and if not disturbed on this late afternoon feeding
flight, they would keep a morning appointment. At about
0700 hours. At dusk they flew back to their river islands for
security and gravel, with not a shot having been fired at them.

I dropped in on Doc Baker later. His eyes lit up like a
schoolboy's when I told him of the flocks.

"What time will we leave?" he asked.

"Five-fifteen too early?"

"I'll be waiting!"

It was a quarter to seven and frosty when we examined

Ed's field, where geese had fed the previous evening. The birch and aspens looked naked, and their last stubborn leaves chattered noisily. A mule deer and her fawn nosed through the crisp-yellow disorder to the edge of the field, flickering ears erect. Farm dogs, like distant geese, barked from the awakening ranches around Marguerite as I staked out two dozen home-made decoys and Doc operated on our blind. Sharp-tailed grouse rose up from the stubble and flew by chuckling. Doc shot an imaginary right and left with deadly accuracy.

It was seven o'clock. Hungry geese honked from the river bars two miles away. Radiation fog filled the river bottom and we knew they would be late for their appointment. From the thermos jug, we poured coffee, enhanced with a sprinkle of Demerara, and started to eat our lunch.

"The decoys look good," Doc said.

I agreed but walked out and straightened the one that he thought should be turned "just a little this way."

It was seven-thirty. Geese honked, airborne, a weather check. "It won't be long now, Doc. Do you want the right or left?"

"This side's good."

"You want to call the shot?"

"No, you call it."

A flock was in the air, honking down the river, gaining altitude. We found them above the fog which was now in patches. Would they turn our way? They did. Twenty-five birds came over the lower fields, up boulder-strewn gulches and forested slopes, into the sun but not directly toward our ambush, thirty yards from the decoys on the edge of the field. They circled the field at one hundred yards; again at eighty. Calling, impression-passing, necks stretching, heads turning. I resisted the temptation to swivel my own head when they flew behind us but kept up a running commentary and gaggle: "At the north end, swinging this way, thirty yards over the fence, gear down, okay."

Doc killed one straight on, as did I. When they broke, flaring in a mad scramble out of their stall, we killed another each. We walked out and picked up our birds. If we didn't shoot any more our day was a success but another flock was on its way. Fifty birds. They circled the field five times, sus-

46

picious, a great old gander at the head. I told Doc to take the
lead bird because I did not think they were going to decoy:
Doc killed him clean and watched him tumble. I killed his
partner and broke the wings on another. The cripple lit out in
the field and ran for the trees. I chased him down though he
ran nearly as fast as I could.

Doc admired his gander. We hefted him and examined his
plumage and large feet and bill. We'd had our sport for the
day. Seven birds. The law said we could take ten. We finished
our coffee and watched flocks cruising the river and fields,
and guessed where they would set down. Five white-fronted
geese came straight in over the trees and landed among the
decoys, neck-stretching, trying to make conversation. We'd
had our goose hunt.

Chapter Six

Minnie the Fisher

"For some of us are out of breath,
And all of us are fat!"

Through the Looking-Glass
Lewis Carroll

Beating a precise tattoo on my poplar, a downy wood-pecker woke me up. I wished he would take his red top-knot elsewhere, but he captured the grub he was after, peered down in a friendly manner, and started on another. The sun in a halo shone weakly through a thin veil of high cirrostratus, indicating that the warm front was developing and we were in for some weather. As confirmation, the wind had veered northerly, but too gradually to be dramatic. Warm fronts seldom last for long at this season, but often bring the definite change to autumn. Slim and Sadsack appeared on the river bank and all was over anyway.

"Sic'm Sack!" yelled Slim, and Sack galloped up, sand and water flying in all directions. His cold nose snorted through and the covers scattered.

"You can sure sleep," Slim said. "It's nearly six-thirty!"

"It's still morning. Hear the geese last night?"

"I sleep when I go to bed."

Slim cleaned the pan-fryers he had just taken from the river. We prefer these small ones for breakfast.

Marked on some maps as two-lane, loose surface, and all-weather, the road climbs steeply from upper Blackwater bridge, and winds between pine-clad ridges high above the glacial meltwater channel. Really, it is just a dirt-and-gravel cow trail that a grader skips over once in awhile. The river is not close by until the neat little Slash ranch on both river banks, a half-mile upriver from Trout Lake Rancheree.

Johnny gave his deep-voiced greeting, and Margaret invited us in for coffee: "Fresh-baked blueberry pie, Bill." The best in the country. Margaret bakes with black-bear fat rendered down for shortening. I know people in New York who have discovered this secret to flaky pastry and have bear grease sent every season. Bruin should have been feasting in berry patches all summer, though, and not on dead salmon, and he must not have been a garbage-dump bum. The hind quarters make fine hams.

Margaret Slash is the last survivor of the Blackwater Indians who lived on the lower river, on Indian Reserves No. 2 and 5 on the north bank above lower Blackwater bridge, and Reserve No. 1, Lesehetcha, on the Fraser two miles above the Blackwater. Her husband, Johnny, is the only one left from his Nataniko or Graveyard Creek village on the western shores of Pelican Lake. A smallpox epidemic around 1895 so thoroughly ravaged the tribes that at some places no one survived to bury the dead. Johnny was a baby a few months old when his uncle, Old Trout Lake Johnny, fortunately found the child, and then raised him a member of the Trout Lake band.

Trout Lake Johnny's age was unknown when he died in 1944. His mother was Etoosnan, who was about eight years old when Alexander Mackenzie's party came through. She spied on them, supposedly, for three days, when they camped near Yimpakluk Lake, close to Dry Lake and Euchiniko Crossing. Did Mackenzie really goof off for three days fishing here and not tell? The Indians appear to have respected Mackenzie highly, but were impressed most with his ability to make fire quickly. Etoosnan died in 1910.

Minnie Trout Lake was visiting Johnny and Margaret.
Minnie is the fisherwoman for the valley, and the best source
for up-to-date fishing information because she knows all the
lakes and streams and keeps them under close observation. If
you ask which is best at the time, you have to make certain
that she understands you to mean best for trout; she herself at
certain times prefers suckers and squawfish. And she knows
the history of each lake for years back.

Thermal stratification, a phenomenon which affects fish
environment, is perhaps analogous to an Angel's Wing, an
after-dinner drink of three dissimilar liqueurs, floating suspended in distinct layers. Lakes stratify too, but without the
color variance. The reason is temperature. The dissolved
oxygen content of each temperature layer varies, and the
variation is the sober concern of crafty fishermen.

The depth of our average Cariboo lakes is about eighty
feet. The surface layer, or the epilimnion, is twenty to twenty-
five feet deep. Temperature may be 70°F or slightly more at
the surface; 68° at the bottom. Oxygen content measures
close to ten parts in a million, top to bottom. The second or
middle layer, the thermocline, extends down through the next
ten to fifteen feet, with temperature close to 68° at the top
and 42° at the bottom. Oxygen content drops quickly, from
eight or nine parts in a million on top to one or less near the
bottom. The third or bottom layer, the hypolimnion,
extends to the bottom of the lake: temperature will be 42°
at the top, but no longer falls quickly, and at the bottom will
likely be 39.2°, but no colder. There will be no oxygen
through most of this layer except at the very top of it—perhaps
0.5 parts in a million.

Fishing below the thermocline under these conditions is
usually a waste of time: trout cannot stay in water depleted of
oxygen. If hot summer weather has prevailed for several days
or weeks the trout are near the top of the thermocline, where
they find tolerable oxygen and temperature. Reefs, bars, and
shallows of twenty to twenty-five feet deep should be favorite
gathering places, especially if cool underground springs
emerge to refresh the rascals and they have an abundance of
hors-d'oeuvres.

Rain supplies some oxygen and wind supplies more to
exposed lakes than to sheltered lakes; and the deeper the lake
the longer the oxygen lasts. Deep mountain lakes, although

they do stratify, will not necessarily be depleted of oxygen in their depths: they can be so deep and so cold that organic decay is retarded and the low oxygen demand is usually replenished by underground flows and streams high in oxygen content. Cold water does retain more oxygen than warm water, but in most lakes the fish and decaying vegetation make great demands. The epilimnion, the top layer, normally receives constant rejuvenation through wind-wave action and photosynthesis, but the temperature barrier of the thermocline confines circulation to the top layer only. As a consequence, the thermocline and hypolimnion receive no additional oxygen from wind, rain, or photosynthesis while this stratification, or summer stagnation, is in effect.

In low-altitude lakes oxygen conditions can become critical. An extended period of extremely hot weather may bring on an olive-green algae "bloom" which not only reduces the photosynthesis process through murkiness, but can also deplete oxygen to such an extent that trout die from suffocation. A combination of conditions generally cause a killing of the fish in summer: decomposing vegetation, logging debris, sawdust, chips and bark, usually combined with domestic sewage pollution, agricultural chemicals and nutrients, or an over-population of fish can cause this summer-kill.

Lake fish can also be killed because of winter water conditions and wind action at spring break-up. Lake water mixes completely just after break-up and again in the fall. Water is most dense, or heaviest, at 39.2°. As water becomes colder than 39.2° it becomes progressively lighter. It then no longer sinks but rises to the surface, and if temperatures drop to 32° the water freezes. These characteristics permit a mixing of the complete water body. With autumn's cooler nights the surface water cools to 39.2° and sinks: fall mixing begins, and summer stagnation ends—temperature and oxygen come to a balance through all depths. In spring, surface water warming to 39.2° again becomes dense and sinks and, assisted by wind-wave action, the spring mixing commences. A strong prevailing wind at break-up may cause this mixing or turnover to go on too rapidly and oxygen-depleted bottom water might dangerously dilute the already meager oxygen supply at the very top. As during a summer-kill, in a winter-kill the fish also die from a lack of oxygen.

52

When winter ice forms a seal, wave action ceases until break-up. The exchange of gases between the air and water also stops and the only remaining source of oxygen is photo- synthesis, but the rate of photosynthesis is regulated by the amount of penetrating light. Under a heavy layer of snow on the ice, the water will be darker than inside Old Joe's outhouse. Even gloomier. A mid-winter Chinook can flood the entire ice surface which will freeze again and leave two layers of ice with several inches of water in between. Sometimes three layers. The penetrating light is reduced even further by fewer hours of sunlight and the lower angle of the sun's rays. The lake rumbles and groans, pops a few air-holes, but takes in no oxygen.

Besides supporting the considerable demands of organic decay, the dissolved oxygen store must support all underwater life. Plants are now consuming instead of producing oxygen. The supply is lowest near the bottom where water temperature is highest, and the supply richest near the top where temperature is lowest–a reversal of summer stagnation. Occasionally these high oxygen demands continue until even the very upper levels cease to support fish.

Because oxygen content varies in different locations throughout the lake, a winter-kill is usually only partial. Coarse fish like suckers and squawfish require less oxygen than do trout and may become the dominant species. Eastern brook trout–which are not true trout but char–are good for restocking because they too require less oxygen. Complete winter-kill occurs most often in small shallow lakes less than about thirty-five feet deep but which are often very productive, though it can happen in large lakes with extensive shallows. Each body of water presents a combination of conditions that may vary from year to year, and even specialists do not always agree on causes of a winter-kill or on the feasibility of preventing it.

Near civilization, winter-killed lakes are restocked if the kill has been severe and they soon produce again. Blackwater lakes, though, depend on natural restocking to recover. Fish come from streams connected to other lakes which did not winter-kill, from a beaver-pond or slough, or early spawners may already be a safe distance up a spawning stream. Because of the amount of food available and the unrestricted living space following a winter-kill, trout growth will be fantastic: after three years the fish often reach ten or fifteen pounds, even larger.

As the cycle continues and fish increase in numbers, the struggle for existence becomes more intense and the average size decreases, especially where good spawning beds encourage over-population. The lake in its natural state will produce only a certain amount of food which can support only so many fish, including the coarse ones. Some lakes are better producers than others but nature, the manager, levels off the size of the fish in proportion to the competition. In naturally overstocked lakes the average size usually increases under heavy fishing pressure because, as fish are harvested, those left have more food. Some productive lakes held countless small trout because the Indians quit netting them many years ago. Then fishing pressure gradually increased the average size to twelve or fourteen inches. Many Blackwater lakes are naturally overstocked. Fishpot, for example. The fish are not huge but do run to seven pounds and average two to four; good for a lake less than a mile long. Indians have netted Fishpot for aeons and if they stopped the lake would swarm with half-starved runts no one would want.

These few years following the winter-killing in a wilderness lake might go unnoticed except by someone like Minnie. She may not understand exactly how winter-kill happens, or why, and certainly knows none of the technical terms, but she does understand the effect. Like most fishermen, Minnie doesn't tell everyone she meets where the big ones are. Most people, though, wouldn't consider her a source of fishing information anyway, whereas she's forgotten more than most anglers will ever learn. She makes part of her living catching fish which she dries and smokes, and has a happy time doing so.

We had met first at the Blackwater bridge where Minnie came by and shyly asked if she could have a ride to Nazko Rancheree. I said sure, but that I was going to catch a few trout first. She giggled her plump pounds.

"You try that place below Joe's." She pointed directions. "On other side the river. Go long by that little house near the fence. It not a smoke-house. Stay above the fence, you okay. Then come to a slick little pond. You find ducks; you sneak. Then go cross the open till you come by those purty red

54

willows, and you see where Joe's mootase been goin. Soon
you come to place Joe keeps raft. Bring it little ways up to
where river swings round. Push real hard, that current take
you to other side. Whoo-ee. Some ride! Then go up little
ways. Good fish stop there." And she sat down by her river
and resumed her weaving of an intricate watape basket as
though she had all the time in the world. When she had it
finished, it would be completely water-tight.

This day at Slash's, Slim and I asked Minnie if she had
fished Chinee Falls lately. No, she hadn't for a long time.

"You try Purty Lake, you got time. Good fish there!
Beaver got water all over that country! You get in okay you
watch where you go. Good raft too that place. Lotsa batnuni
at Euchiniko Lake. But better I think at Kloo-kah-nee-wa,
what you call Upper Euchiniko Lake, they feed ten men."

"We'll be leaving the pick-up at Husee, Johnny. If somebody who can drive comes by, we'd appreciate his leaving it
at the bridge."

"Okay. We'll see what we can do."

Chapter Seven

Big
Nose

*"The face is what one goes by, generally,"
Alice remarked in a thoughtful tone.*

Through the Looking-Glass
Lewis Carroll

Peter Morris of Kluskus said that in 1897 his father, Old Chief Morris, killed the first moose, or "dunee" as he called it, seen in their territory. This is the earliest account of moose in the watershed. Because they were not acquainted with the animal and considered it "dionike" or bad, none of the band would eat the meat except Old Jerome, the Chief's brother, who had encountered moose before. The next moose, according to the Indians, was killed by Captain Harry of Ulkatcho in 1903. Trout Lake Alex shot the first seen in his area, in 1910; Johnny Slash's tribe refused to eat it. By this time several had been shot near Batnuni Lake and in the upper Euchiniko region. The herd was well established in the Blackwater by 1916–large moose, the horns of many bulls were immense.

57

Until the turn of the century, moose were confined by habitat to more northerly regions of the Province, but during the early years of settlement in Central British Columbia huge fires levelled extensive stands of mature conifer forest. Consequently, the moose expanded southward into the ideal new deciduous growth. The mule deer, too, spread out and increased.

The conditions that created abundant range for moose were nearly disastrous for the original animal inhabitants, the woodland caribou or "whet-zae" of the Blackwater Indians. Their habitat was destroyed. Prior to 1880 or thereabouts, judging from Indian stories and the number of horns still found at old cabins, swamps, and meadows, caribou were numerous over all the upper Blackwater basin. When the succession of uncontrolled fires wiped out most of their winter range, these herds declined. Later prospectors burned off the alpines to expose bedrock. Fires do not always destroy the timber but do consume the lichens and mosses and humis and leave barren rock near or below the treeline where caribou stay during wet weather and most of the winter. Lichens are one of the slowest-growing and longest-lived of vegetations; they require several decades to re-establish and in that area are only now approaching a supply sufficient to support caribou. This change in habitat is a profound illustration of how a species will multiply to the capacity of new and suitable range while another, following the destruction of its habitat, will disappear, an illustration of just how dependent wild life is upon the land.

Paradoxically there is a time and place for a forest fire. The Indians learned many years ago to set fires to improve both their hunting and their berry crops, but moose and other wildlife now depend on "natural" or "unplanned" forest fires for food. Improved winter food supplies for deer have also come about through logging operations which also open up the forest and create food in a more or less natural manner, but in interior British Columbia, at least, mature timber as well as food is vital to the winter survival of deer. Climax forests provide housing or shelter. But many key shelter areas have been logged off, and although there is plenty of food for deer there are few deer to eat it for they have lost their home.

58 The grasslands of British Columbia also once supported a

large population of elk, or "ya-zie." In the early 1800's, and precisely when is unknown, some calamity like a killer winter or series of them decimated the herds from the Rocky Mountains to the Pacific; early settlers plowed up elk horns as far south as Langley. During the winter of 1948 two Nazko Indians thought they found the tracks of two-year-old cattle, but when tracking proved the men to be wrong they decided to continue, and near the source of Axe Creek, north of The Mountain, they came on seven elk. For several years reports of elk sightings have trickled in, and now sightings are no longer rare although elk have not yet regained a fraction of their former range.

The Blackwater is a region of temperature extremes, but has no official met recording stations. At Quesnel airport, at 1,788 feet altitude, the annual precipitation over a twenty-year average is 21.34 inches. Snowfall averages 73.9 inches. The heaviest monthly precipitation occurs in August, with about three inches, followed by January with about twenty-three inches of snow. The driest month is May with 1.37 inches, followed by September with 1.55 inches. At Williams Lake airport the average annual hours of bright sunshine—unrecorded at Quesnel—is 2,127, second only to Gonzales Observatory, Victoria, which has the highest average in the Province.

Since annual precipitation in the watershed is probably less than twenty-five inches, timber is only moderately heavy and undergrowth relatively spare. Dominant broad-leaved trees are trembling aspen and Western white birch. Also water birch, black cottonwood, Douglas maple, Sitka and mountain alder, mountain ashes, several species of willow and willow-like shrubs, and the various serviceberries. Coniferous trees are mainly lodgepole pine and Western white spruce, but also Engelmann and black spruce, alpine fir or balsam-fir, whitebark pine, and Rocky Mountain juniper. A few tamaracks grow in the swamps of the Euchiniko. Most of the basin lies out of fir-type country and Douglas fir is generally confined to the lower section of the watershed, although a few small stands do grow near Kluskus. The last large fir one sees in the Blackwater basin, when one is riding west to Dean River, is the great gnarled tree near the trail on the southeastern slope of Poplar Mountain.   59

Following a wet spring and a moderately wet early summer, the swamps, muskegs, and lakes swarm with mosquitoes, but hot weather soon kills them off. In the higher ranges during July and August, and sometimes in early September, there are usually at least some black flies and bulldogs, the "light and bite" type, which can have the necks of some riders raw above the shirt collar before they have covered many miles. Most moose seek lakes to escape insects and to feed on pond lily roots, but some mature bulls herd on the high country in July and August. In some years the woodland caribou inhabiting the rolling country around and above timberline, about 5,500 feet in these latitudes, have problems living with the botfly. Not dependent upon water to the extent of moose, mule deer range the breeze-blown slopes and semi-alpines. All seem well able to adapt to their discomfort, although some years must be trying.

In mid-winter, Chinook winds often sweep in from the southwest and within hours send temperatures soaring from forty below to forty above. The Chinooks that pass over this region carry warm, moist, air and, while softening and sometimes melting the snow, pick up very little moisture. By the time a Chinook has risen over the Rocky Mountains to the foothill country on the eastern slope the air has become relatively dry and the wind removes snow and moisture almost by magic. In the Blackwater woods a prolonged mid-winter thaw is a curse. Travel becomes next to impossible. Snowshoeing during a Chinook can be a small catastrophe. I peel off my woolies and camp until a freeze tightens up the land again, camp, and enjoy the balm-drenched countryside and the semi-hibernating creatures who stir from their burrows to see if spring has really arrived.

This freakish weather coming when four or five feet of snow cover the ground, and prevailing for two or three days and nights, brings extreme hardship to game animals, for when normal near-zero temperatures follow the snow becomes heavily encrusted. In their search for food, animals must then break a glasslike sheath which cuts hocks and leaves blood in tracks. The animals become weak, and the diseased and old become easy prey for wolves who are now able to run on the hard surface.

60   I have several times then seen over-populated moose and

deer winter-range: herds increased to the limit of the food
resources; a prolonged killer winter; animals forced to remain at lower levels. Snow piled deep in early November
forces herds down to lower levels weeks ahead of normal,
and there the herds remain. Heavy snows and low temperatures might continue for many weeks, except for the occasional Chinook. By early April nearly all animals will be approaching a state of malnutrition and will be fighting to
survive, and spring, which normally allows them to spread out
for food again, might come late.

Central British Columbia deer herds border northern
range limitations and during these hard winters and late
springs I have trailed through mule deer winter ranges and
could scarcely find a healthy specimen. Humped-up does,
with their few frosty-faced fawns just bags of bones, and their
stomachs full of abortion-producing growth that deer should
never have to eat. Low resistance to sickness and parasites:
April on the way, weeks until green growth comes for the
survivors. Spring die-offs then happen easily; the small number of yearling browsers reflects the high winter losses, for the
young are the first to go. The females abort and, in spring,
there is a high mortality among the runted newborn in the
herd. The overbrowsed winter range is severely damaged and
may then take several years to regain its vigor, if it ever fully
does. The upland willows and red osier dogwoods, and small
aspen and birch lie broken, too severely "pruned" by the
moose; the firs are "high-lined" as far up as deer can reach.

Antlerless hunting seasons based on factual information
help prevent this waste by reducing the herd through the
cropping of more animals, protecting the wintering grounds
from over browsing, and keeping the herd healthy and productive. Better to have fewer animals, but to have some extra
range as insurance against a killer winter. Unfortunately,
during an antlerless season any deer is legal, and this results
in the cropping of the animal group which is of primary
importance to the herd – the dry females – and a normal,
healthy herd always has a fairly large number of them.

A doe deer or cow moose that is "dry" is one that has failed
to bring offspring through summer to fall, or is a young
animal that will give birth for the first time next year. Those
which lost young in the spring usually lost them very soon

after they were born. Dry females, since they are without fawns or calves to hinder them, pass the summer and fall in good condition, and will therefore survive a killer winter better than will any member of the herd. The dry animals of one summer almost always have young the following spring, and because of the fitness of the mother these youngsters will be the hardiest and healthiest produced. Following extreme winter conditions, therefore, this dry, antlerless group is the crutch of the herd because, under normal conditions, it builds quality.

Most revenue created through hunting is spent on protecting wildlife from hunters, but unfortunately an antlerless season invites the least knowledgeable of the hunting society, those who feel no twinge of conscience at engaging in plain senseless slaughter. They think it their right to kill bear cubs, fawns, herons, loons, marsh hawks, owls, eagles, foxes, beavers, marmots, pikas; blow them apart and leave them to rot in the woods. Such wildlife is valueless to them. Hunters mention little of the wounded and lost game. Lousy shots "flock-shooting" deer at 500 yards: broken legs, shot-up meat, gut-shot cripples never hunted down. Hunters too lazy to climb a hill to see if any are wounded.

I've checked hundreds of hunters and watched hundreds more, and though hunting is not inhumane, some of the hunters are. Unless organized sportsmen clean up their sport, those who consider hunting inhumane will do so for them. Neither proficiency nor equipment, let alone knowledge of our wild life, is anywhere near a decent standard. Very many "hunters" go into the woods only once or twice a year. Only a fool would go where they carry out their mayhem. Probably the deer and moose too, the entire wildlife community, would prefer a winter kill to an antlerless season when the waste is so severe. I stay away from these "hunting" places now, I fly to the boondocks to enjoy nature taking care of her own.

For several months, ranchers and game guides and many hunters had reported a pack of wolves operating from Nazko and Pelican to Pantage and Milburn Lakes, a pack which had been roaming the plateau near several ranches but had killed no stock. Pressured into eliminating them, Sadsack, Pokey the horse, and I headed west. The snow got progressively

deeper the higher we climbed The Mountain. Pokey was

chest-deep in the drifts and sometimes had to bound through. *Big*
I stopped frequently and moose-watched to prevent his being *Nose*
too sweated up. Sadsack trailed along behind, carrying my
snowshoes and his own little pack.

I was wondering whether we'd reach Open Hole cabin
without spending a night under the stars when something
appeared ahead of us. It had emerged from a snow-swirl, just
popped out of a snowdrift, a red-nosed, grey-bearded gnome
on a spry little horse. The hound-dog ear-flaps of his muskrat
hat flopped with the horse; bear-skin chapps reached down to
his mukluks, and a beaver coat covered the in-between.
Where did shaggy horse stop and man begin? Not supersti-
tious enough to think him the Guardian Spirit of The Mountain, I knew the eastern terminus of the moccasin telegraph
had caught up to me. I recognized the sorrel cayuse and knew
the rider frozen to him had to be Old Joe. The horse was
stepping lively. Joe's formula was to "Lettem have a shotta
snoose once in awhile, and they'll never be troubled with
worms!"

He had once lost this sorrel to the wild bunch of horses up
on The Desert, where the horse had come from originally and
the Indians had taken two years to get him back for Joe.
"You can't kill this smart li'l ugly cayuse," Joe said afterward. "Those fancy ones are okay, but gimme one born to the
country. They got guts to pull through a tough one! It's up to
them. They don't suffer. An he's sure t'hell being looked
after, the knothead! I think he's mostly moose, but he doesn't
havta eat rip-gut! And this slab-sided slick's beginning to
understand he see more country with me than on his own."

"Where ya headed?" he roared through the swirls.

"Up on The Mountain to see the wolves!" I yelled back,
just to make him feel good.

"Lotsa white stuff up there," he said quietly. But then
hollered back, "I'm not deaf! Took me three days to come
this far. Never seen so much snow! You going to kill those
wolfs with poison? You got anything to drink?"

I fished a flask of 151-proof from a saddlebag and settled
back to watch him gasp, but he didn't bat an eye, and I told
him that I didn't know whether I'd kill them, but that some
ranchers had been complaining all fall and winter. I asked
him if this bunch had killed any cattle that he knew of.   63

"No. I don't know of any being killed," he said quietly. "Those wolfs travel a long ways. Ten of them. They travel from out Kluskus way, down Baezaeko, Chinee Falls. From The Mountain they cut over to the Musquash and Blackwater, and I see their tracks over on the Euchiniko. I hear they been over to Batnuni. Minnie say they been to her place, and Little Charlie Cremo saw them at Big Meadow."

"Would you kill them, Joe?"

"No. They don't do any harm. None yet, anyway."

"I'll take a look. They seem to hang near The Mountain a lot."

"I broke the trail for ya. I think Little Jimmy Lick's coming through with Paul's freighting sleigh. Maybe you meet him. You find lotsa deer in that balsam-fir timber north of the road."

"Deer, Joe?"

"Yeah, deer! You deaf or somethin'?" This was news to me. I didn't think any deer wintered within forty miles of this lodgepole pine wilderness.

"Sure. Good place for mouich to hang out," he said in answer to my doubt, letting a decisive squirt of snoose almost get Sack. "Springs on that mountain never freeze. Funny place. Must be hot springs melt off the snow in places and bare-off some green stuff for them. They stop there all winter in good shape. I get once in awhile a little one. Maybe you see some elk, too. Yesus, that's strong rum you got!"

Paul's freight cabin at Open Hole looked good when we arrived that evening. It was about fifteen below when I put Pokey in the small barn at the back. Little Jimmy Lick's four-horse team was in there and with the five animals it was nice and warm. After dinner Jimmy produced a glare-proofed deck of cards and asked if I'd like a quiet game of poker. His wife was busy putting the kids to bed on the other side of the one-room cabin, and somehow Sack had got into the act. Little Jimmy is even quieter than Little Charlie and the game was a quiet one all right. He cleaned me of what change I had, as well as of some folding money. "You purty good poker-player, I think," said Jimmy, pocketing my money. The big over-statement of the evening.

Finding wolf tracks was easy because the pack had visited Open Hole the day before, licked out some of Paul's discarded sardine cans, sniffed Joe's perilous snoose squirts, and played with an old moose hide and some cardboard boxes. Following their trail north of the road we soon found ourselves in a climax alpine fir and spruce forest, some trees three feet through. The whole nature of the country changed. This small knob had escaped the fires that had swept by on all sides in past years and its virgin timber was an oasis. After snowshoeing to the summit, I boiled a pot of tea and in bright February sunshine enjoyed the view and the quiet sounds of deep woods in winter. The snow-laden landscape rolled to the clear horizon with an overwhelming sense of space. Nearly 5,000 feet here, the highest point of land for miles.

Through the four or five miles of timber I'd crossed, I estimated about 100 wintering deer; a small pocket. There was about five feet of fairly loose snow and the herd had what I call jump-trails, trails looking like flights of stairs up and around the hillsides. Having had no new snow for several days, the surface was littered with tiny wind-blown fir fragments with strands of usnea lichen clinging to them. The deer having a lichen feast seemed in good condition for February, and the wolves hadn't bothered any of them. A winter deer haven.

To the north-west, a Boreal Forest raven voiced his presence several times during the morning, an invitation to all wild creatures. Thought to sometimes reach the age of 100 years, the raven rivals the goose and eagle for longevity, and for intelligence, and he figures prominently in native mythology and culture; if dying to become a legend, shoot a raven in Indian territory. He is usually apart from other ravens in the winter, but seems to enjoy the company of wolves and a variety of forest creatures. His musical croak, with its wide range of sounds, echoes through the silence, telling of the kill and what is going on around it.

We had taken a different route back around the knolls to see what was on the menu and, as I thought it would, raven's satisfied bell changed to a warning croak as soon as he spotted us. A cow and calf moose had been killed by the wolves, and were within thirty feet of one another. About three days old, half the kill was already eaten. We circled around to determine who had been previous visitors: foxes and coyotes had dined there; one wolverine, one fisher, two

marten, two or three short-tailed weasels, and a few red
squirrels; chickadees, jays, and the raven.

We were too late for a proper visceral examination but I
cracked a femur of the calf, a poorly, runted animal. The
bone marrow which would be pearly-pink in a healthy
animal was bright red, a sure sign of advanced malnutrition.
A femur from the cow showed even greater fat depletion. She
was very old, and small, and had badly worn teeth. Some
jawbone disease was present. Contagious warts on her legs
and face must have interfered with her vision. We probably
would have found hard, golf-ball-sized hydatid tapeworm
cysts in the lungs for there were lung adhesions in the chest
cavity. The wolf pack had really performed community service: the cow would not have seen another summer; the calf,
perhaps, but bearing its mothers inflictions. Poison seemed
unnecessary. Dogs or wolves, coyotes or cougar eating the
infected tissue pass the hydatid tapeworm eggs through the
faeces to man. There is no danger to humans from the moose.

At Open Hole that night the first timber wolf moaned
about nine o'clock. Sack and I climbed up on the barn roof in
order to better hear the wild chorus that followed. Low-
pitched moans rising in shifting falsettoes were prolonged or
suddenly terminated. Wildly off-key, the melody grew to
wails and yodels, a primitive refrain through the frost-
sparkled night. I was uncertain whether the musicale was
stationary, or was being re-echoed against the hills from two
directions. Sack thought we were surrounded. He wasn't
afraid; he was shivering sick! I pointed up a pine and told him
I'd seen a cougar. When he fell off the roof in his excitement,
and stopped howling, from the shadows a few hundred feet
away came a coaxing whine. Not interested! He'd heard that
one before.

In the morning we checked the poison stations. Eight
wolves were dead. Two had left the pack, to raise a family I
hoped. No longer would the pack calls echo through the
valleys from Kluskus to Blackwater and the moose herd
would be the biggest losers.

Little Charlie was waiting for Slim and me at Husee, or
Chop Creek, which is five miles northwest of Trout Lake
66 Rancheree and on Indian reserve land. Because the creeks

and water holes freeze during winter, people must chop
through the ice to water horses or cattle. The few water holes
that never freeze therefore have names: Moose Springs; Open
Hole; Tetachuck, really a ford about knee-deep that remains
open in winter. Cows save a lot of their grudges for the water
hole and running a good watering place and keeping it safe is
quite an art. If the arrangement is wrong a cow can slip, roll
over on her back and never get up.

At Husee you have to chop a hole in winter, but in the fall
there are several moose burns nearby and small lakes and
swamp meadows. The place is a moose-crossing. At least the
Indians camp here when after their winter supply of meat,
much of which they cut into thinly sliced strips and smoke-
dry into jerky on the spot. Hide, stomach, intestines, nose,
tongue, bone marrow, all have a use. When finished with the
carcasses, the encampment leaves nothing much but the
hoofs, sometimes horns. In ancient times the jerky was pulverized and, after fat and dried berries had been added, the
mixture, which was called pemmican, was sewn into bags
twelve to eighteen inches in diameter and buried under the
ground for hard times. On the Fraser, along with two bags of
wild rice and a gallon keg of gunpowder, Mackenzie had
hidden a bag of pemmican weighing ninety pounds. He
wanted to be sure of something to eat when he returned from
his trip to the Pacific, and pemmican keeps as well as cannon
balls and is about as hard. Ranchers who settled on ancestral
camp grounds plowed the bags up. Walt Merz, who ranched
at Four Mile near Quesnel, used to find them, but though he
never ate one they appeared still to be in good condition. He
kept a few in the root-cellar, just in case.

Once at Husee I saw my largest rack of horns on the hoof.
This bull survived the meeting because Little Charlie and I
had lost track of the days. We weren't entirely sure the season
was open and though I called a pow-wow, Charlie didn't
help: "Drop him! He's big and fat." Conscience won. Actually the season had opened that morning and a camp of
Indian hunters would have put the meat to good use. I still
have visions of this bull standing broadside at a hundred
yards, and of the flash of sun on his horns when he turned and
trotted off.

"That's a good-looking buckskin," I said to Charlie, commenting on the saddle horse which was tied to the tailboard of his wagon when we met at Hussee. "Who'd you trade?"

"Trade Old Lashaway Sandyman. Good trade."

"Tough trader too! What do you call him?"

"Just Horse," he shrugged. "Horse his name," Charlie advised with finality. "He's all horse. Sometimes I call him Yesle, his Indian name."

We loaded our gear and canoe on the wagon and set off on the trail to Dry Lake. We had fast going for about four miles until we reached the spruce swamps south of Cotsworth Lake. These quagmires would almost swallow a four-wheel-drive vehicle but they just slowed Charlie down. South of Kluskus Crossing on the Euchiniko we reached the fire-killed trees of which we had been warned. Power saw screaming, Slim cut the deadfalls and I threw the sections off the trail.

This burn was created by a cattleman who thought he was improving the range. Some areas south of Euchiniko River were only scorched, and the trees fell for many years after, but the main fire so thoroughly burned the area from Euchiniko River to the outskirts of Vanderhoof that its five-to twenty-five-mile-wide swath became known as The Desert. The fire created winter moose food, but the area was never overly popular with these animals. It was too large and had few patches of timber: ideal moose country has small burns, of various ages, with contiguous areas of forest cover.

Truly this was a desert, but a decidedly interesting one. Initially the area reforested itself in broad-leaved trees, willows and shrubs. Saskatoon, blueberry, huckleberry, red currant, blackcap, gooseberry, cloudberry, crowberry, and bog and mountain cranberry grew in profusion. Much of this area is a wintering ground for willow ptarmigan, who like the bog-birch cranberry patches. Wild rose, honeysuckle, strawberry, clover, soopalallie, kinnikinik. The area was now ideal for the sharp-tailed grouse, commonly called prairie chicken, but which is not a true prairie chicken. A spring dancing ground was located on a knoll near Dry Lake. Hunting was simple: birds would perch by the dozen all around a camp.

Undoubtedly this burn did temporarily improve the habitat for the wild horse band which roams the country between
Titetown Lake, and the Chilako River where the Indians

have built corrals at strategic locations to capture a few of the animals. The Indians turned a good sorrel stud in with these slicks some years ago and have shot many of the scrubs. As a result some are now fair horses: long-legged, tough cayuses which rustle well, but are mean and hard to handle. Za-Louie and I hunted them once, but a puff of dust heading for Mud River was all we saw.

After about two hours work we emerged from the tangle, passed the side trail to Yimpakluk or Trout Lake, and before we started up Poplar Mountain I collected some mushrooms in Alexander Mackenzie's "basons." On July 8, after camping with some Indians near Dry Lake, he had reported that he was surprised to see "several regular basons." Some had held water and some were dry, their depth about twelve feet, their gravel edges sloped at an angle of about forty-five degrees. The dry ones had been covered with grass and herbs, mustard and mint.

There are four basins beside the Grease Trail, just south of the east end of Titetown Lake. They are circular, about one hundred yards across, like bomb craters. Most likely they had formed around blocks of ice which had become isolated during the waning stages of the ice cap. As the glaciers melted rapidly, the streams spewed sand and gravel around the ice block, and when the blocks melted the kettle remained. The shallow depressions now occupied by many small plateau lakes and ponds were formed in much the same way. Some of the glacial meltwater channels on Poplar Mountain, directly to the west, now carry small streams.

Chapter Eight

Purty Rainbows

*"Do all that you know, and try all that you don't:
Not a chance must be wasted to-day!"*
"The Hunting of the Snark"
Lewis Carroll

A fully forged thunderstorm was steadily approaching, with turreting cumulonimbus spread across the top in classical anvil shape and scud-roll boiling at the leading edge. Deceptive white heads reared columns in line above several black decks. Spawned over the Pacific expanse, nudged with a tail wind, the fury sped eastward. Thunder muttered through the assault and violent blasts oscillated against the mountain slopes. All became quiet, waiting.

"We're in for a galvanizing," Slim predicted.

"Shall we camp?" I asked. It would be dark before we reached Chinee Falls and we could pitch the tent here before the rain hit.

"This Purty Lake Creek," said Charlie. "Lotsa horse feed this place."

71

A small stream crossed the trail and ran bank-full across a poplar flat and down a coulee to another flat below and into a meadow-bordered lake. We found a good location in groves of aspen and birch with no high trees. Lightning ripped the sky overhead. Rain deluged us. Hail slapped the tent and bounced with a deafening roar. A jagged fork stabbed from the black base of the storm, probed for a group of nearby trees, and filled the air with ozone.

"Did you time that one?" I asked Slim.

"We're in the safest place, I think," he replied.

"When it lets up what do you say we try Purty Lake? Minnie's been netting ten-pounders there," I said.

"We have rain gear. Why wait?"

"Bad place for lightning," Charlie warned. "Big storm!"

"We'll wait awhile longer," Slim conceded.

By examining our air photos and topographic maps we leisurely explored the physiography of this little-known landscape as it looked from 18,000 feet. The extensive glacial gouging had provided depressions for the hundreds of large and small lakes now occupying the Nechako and Fraser Plateaux. A chain of small lakes lay along the southern slope of Poplar Mountain.

"Must be trout in all of them," said Slim. "We're going to walk to the lake, Charlie. Are you coming?"

"I'll stop in camp this time. Minnie says raft over by meadow."

The storm moderated and we started out but, because the horse trail was flooded by beaver, we walked in the fringe of timber. Two miles in, the lake lay below slopes of poplar and birch and scattered pines. Surging trout broke the silence. We rigged up with floating lines and hefty leaders.

Minnie's raft was a typical Indian raft—long, narrow of beam, easily paddled. I guided Slim to within casting distance of the rises, over a shallows with heaped-up chara ringed by tules. A trout, a rainbow of about eight pounds, rose up through the clear water and smashed the fly on the first cast, leaped four times in rapid succession, bore for open water, and was gone.

"He's got my fly!" Slim exclaimed.

I flipped mine out to the swirl of a rise and was ready when one came. The trout leaped, tail-walked, shook himself,

leaped again, and ran past the raft for deep water. I almost
lost a finger. He had half my backing out before he slowed
down. Slim paddled after the fish and I gradually worked him
alongside and Slim netted him.

"Nine or ten pounds," he announced, before releasing him
"Fat and deep."

We returned to the weed-bed but the light breeze had
backed 180°, and not a rise to be seen. Slim cast again and
again. I changed to the spool with sinking line and handed it
to him. He cast out about seventy feet, let it sink, and
retrieved slowly. I held the raft stationary at the edge of the
dropoff. The fly was almost to the raft when a fish streaked
after it. When we released him we guessed him to be eleven
or twelve pounds. Like the first, he was deep and powerful.

Slim and I use a net for the larger trout. It is more consider-
ate of the fish, for with a net we needn't play them completely
out before releasing them. Even when taken with care, they
sometimes need assistance to recover while they regain
oxygen and enough vigor to cruise away, but they will
survive if they do not bleed or if their internal organs are not
bruised. A fish has no blood to spare. Bait fishermen, salmon
roe specialists in particular, often find their hooks embedded
in the top of the fish's stomach and he bleeds profusely.

The wind, which hadn't exceeded five knots at any time,
veered 180° again and trout began feeding on the surface
once more. But black sheets of rain thrashed the water;
lightning struck the mountain top and forked toward an
osprey's nest: we weren't safe on the lake. We landed on
shore and lit a fire.

Sack came through the pines and joined us, shaking himself and spreading a fog of skunk all around. While investigating a stump the previous week he had become involved
with a woods-pussy who shot first and asked questions later.
I had doused Sack in tomato juice and had given him a bath,
then sprayed him with foo-foo camouflage but when he was
wet the skunk smell still hung like a cloud. "You stink!" I told
him. He examined himself seriously and looked up as if to say
"I can't help it; can't stand myself either."

The storm lasted half an hour. We fished farther down the
lake, sometimes using the sinking line outfit and sometimes
the floating, but always catching fish.

No other sport can replace fishing, and the time to go
fishing is when the spirit stirs and one can steal off. Not wait
for weather to settle, temperature to rise or fall, or the moon
to cast its shadow across the boss's planet. Weather elements
do influence the fishing but staying put because one element
does not appear exactly right is wasting leisure time.

A fly rod and reel and line is a unit, each in proper balance
with the others. For a rod, I like the very best in split cane,
but in place of cheap cane I'd rather fish with a good fiberglass rod, although I've yet to use fiberglass with action
comparable to cane. A rod should have strength and fast
recovery in the tip, with comparable action through to the
butt. A rod that casts effortlessly is a good rod. And a good
rod, even of fiberglass, should be treated with loving care.
Most fly-fishermen would as soon lend their best girl. I
always avoid storing my wet rod in an airtight travelling case,
because the combination of heat and moisture can quickly
cook the rod and cause it to become unglued, brittle, and
weak. The reel should be sturdy, but as light as possible, and
big enough to allow for plenty of backing behind the fly line.
Since I fly-fish for steelhead as well as for trout, I have two
Hardy reels of different sizes, each with a spare drum. Some
fishermen take two complete outfits, but like firearms, each
outfit has its own nuance and a man becomes accustomed to
a favorite. In lines, I prefer a double-taper in either floating
or sinking. I store the floaters on my reels and the sinkers on
my spare spools, and make a fast switch when necessary. My
No. 8 lines, with my nine-foot rod, will cast as far as the No.
10 lines with my Hardy steelhead rod. This heavy Hardy has
become progressively weaker through years of fish and soggy
lines, and now handles the No. 10 better than it formerly
handled the equivalent of a No. 11. Both rigs will cast ninety
feet, but distance is not all-important.

Rigged in this fashion, my expenses are minimal. Leaders
are not expensive, the tapered nine- or ten-footers. Flies can
be expensive but need not be. Better to spend money on
hooks. Fly-tying is really over-rated: even a novice can put
up some very fishy numbers.

Besides his equipment, knowledge of insects is important
to a fly-fisherman. A good fly fisherman is an opportunist
74 who reasons out why the fish are not interested in his way of

fishing and then acts in accord with reason. He knows, in
particular, that most trout food in streams and lakes is
aquatic life, nymph-type food, not yet metamorphosed to the
fly stage. Or it is permanent underwater life (those insects
who live out their lives underwater). At times, certain
nymphs are particularly abundant; readily available to the
fish, they could be considered an underwater hatch. He
knows, too, that rainbow trout can be great excavators. At
times they root in the bottom of a lake for all types of food,
especially in the shallows over a marl bottom or over the sort
of bottom which looks like some place a loon would get
stuck. Dragon-fly and damsel-fly nymphs, mayfly, stone,
alder and caddis are their favorite foods, or small snails and
leeches, and the shrimp which burrow under debris after a
courtship.

I try to know my lake and what is going on around it, what
is in the water, what is crawling to the bank, what is flying,
and what is in the stomach of my fish. Fishermen who do not
know these little facts miss days and days of sport. And
fishermen can learn a few of the facts by going out at night
and shining a powerful flashlight to the bottom of ten or
twenty feet of water. Stirring the bottom with a pole makes
the nymphs and leeches scurry, and shows what kind of
action you should be trying for if you want to catch fish when
they have so much natural feed anyway. That is, if the lake is
not polluted.

In some lakes on some summer days there just doesn't
seem to be a fish. Or else he is on a strict plankton diet. Fish
are there, of course, at least in the lakes I fish, but what else
are the slippery rascals feeding on? Ignore such questions,
and ignore comments like "the lake's gone off" or "it's no
sooner come on than its gone off" or "too hot" or "no fish."
Set the creative mechanism in motion: rig the pole, swim the
fly to them, and accept conditions as they are. Catch the
fellows by using a line of a specific gravity which will reach to
the thermocline, especially in mid-summer when a lake is flat
and glassy.

Nymph-style fishing with a sinking line is new to some
people and beginners will not appreciate this modern line as
much as will old-timers. Dry-fly purists who must see the
swirl as the trout rises do not enjoy fishing with this line

either, for the fly is fished deep, often only inches from the bottom, and is worked in slowly. The technique is not perhaps as soul-satisfying as dry-fly fishing, but one prerequisite is patience: if fishing properly you will be a long time between casts. Another prerequisite is a sensitive touch: a trout can spit out a fly in a split second.

For the lakes I usually fish while anchored at the drop-off, or over a weed-bed, shoal, or reef, I do not like a "fast" sinking line which is hard to control when retrieving. It settles too quickly and will hook up on the bottom or in the weeds. I prefer a "medium" sinker which settles fast enough to keep the action going, yet will clear the bottom when long-spaced and short retrieves are necessary. A very fast sinker is of value when fishing steelhead or Dolly Varden.

A long bold cast is an advantage, and the delicate, accurate presentation necessary in dry-fly fishing is not quite so important. A feeler will usually find the depth at which the fish are feeding, at perhaps only a few feet. A crystal-clear lake allows watching the fly sink and watching the fish cruise the depths, and allows noting how quickly the line reaches the different levels.

Some of the best flies for submerged fishing are dressings on large hooks, on number sixes or fours for weight, perhaps even weighted on the shank as well. The various Careys are good standbys: in black, yellow, orange, green or red bodies, some full-bodied and full-feathered, others more sparingly dressed. They are simple to tie up and nearly always take fish. The Shrimp, the Doc Spratley, the Leech tied in black or dark-brown forms, and the aqueous insects like the free-swimming boatman, are all good too. But names are confusing. We should be concerned with types rather than names. Personally, I can scarcely identify twenty flies with any accuracy and probably haven't all of those in my boxes.

In fishing as in hunting the real pleasure comes in the stalk, which requires patience, thought, and knowledge. Often just walking to a pool or anchoring over a shoal and starting in to fish is not enough for me. I like to choose my victim and see if I can catch him, especially at a small lake that supports a few, hard-to-catch, large fish. These are the fish I remember.

I sometimes fish a lake which is reached from a winding
slough so overgrown with lilies that wiggling through in a

canoe doesn't appear to be possible. It is really a pond four
hundred yards across. A shelf drops quickly to sixty feet. A
trickle which empties in from a poplar and spruce swamp
never runs dry, and is large enough and has sufficient gravel
for limited spawning. Ten to fifteen pounders here. Unknown
to each other, Doc Baker and I had both fished it for years.

I like to glide in to the edge and soak up the surroundings
before wetting the line. While conscious thought lies suspended, while it is being replaced by the quiet life of the
pond, the world goes on around me. But if fish are rising I
will spot them and there are usually one or two.

On one occasion, when thus creatively engaged, I saw the
largest cow moose I have ever seen, and with her was the
smallest new calf. It was springtime. Golden-eye, buffle head,
horned grebe, a pair of each on the lake. Blackbirds scolded
from the tules, ruffed grouse drummed in the forest, a poor-
will lamented, the bittern pumped out the lake.

A trout was feeding on the damsel flies rustling among the
tules. I had watched him rising most of the late afternoon. In
half-an-hour it would be dark. He started rising again. I
examined a garish blue, polar bear streamer fly dressed on a
No. 2 hook with a long shank. Travel-worn, too large, outlandish. A fly-fisherman's conversation piece, admired but
never swum. A bewitching something I'd perhaps offer a
heathen Dolly Varden languishing at the bottom of a pool
and eating every titbit in sight. I primped it, sharpened the
hook, tied it on.

I slipped out of my lair, uncoiled fifty or so feet of line, laid
some out behind, and waited. He rose. At the edge of the
lilies. I gave it to him. There was a boil and I had him fast.
Nearly finishing me near a submerged tree, he took me
through the lily pads, and into the slough. I finally netted
him, hefted him, and then let him go.

"It's late and I'm starved," I reminded Slim for the third
time.

"Yeah. Guess we'd better call it quits. I c'd spend a week
around this chain."

A broad, close-coupled bull moose in the fifty-inch cate-
gory trotted across the meadow, his long bell swinging from
side to side. Stringy pieces of velvet still clung to his antlers.

"How'd you like that guy in your freezer?" Slim asked.

"He'll be on the prod soon."

Nature exercises wondrous stratagems. A bull moose eats little if any food during the rut and keeps on the move in search of a cow. An early winter catches him with practically no fat. On the other hand, if the fall is open he will again be in fair condition by December. Though much easier to hunt when crazed by the rut, for choice meat he should be killed in August or very early September. For this reason early hunting is permitted in the more remote areas.

"Anything exciting happen, Charlie?"

"Cayuses staked out little ways. Better they stay close tonight."

Nimbostratus cloud which had followed the storm was clearing away and stars winked through. Charlie's campfire felt good and the fragrance of Hudson's Bay 151 in the Purty Creek water blended pleasantly with the surroundings. We grilled steaks over willow coals and sautéed "bason" mushrooms. Sack ate a four-pound trout and pulverized the steak bones. The eiderdown came shortly afterwards. A rain shower pattered the tent. Reels sang and boisterous rainbows leaped beryl waters.

Chapter Nine

Up the
Grease Trail

And the bellman, sagaciously nodding his head,
Said "That must depend on the weather."

"The Hunting of the Snark"

Lewis Carroll

I awoke to horse bells clanging, Sack barking, and Slim yelling "Head 'em off, Charlie! They're goin' for the tent." I grabbed my duds and scrambled for the doorway and the tent pole went over. Spooked horses would flatten the works any moment. Outside, Slim and Charlie, with a horse bell in each hand, were laughing like idiots. Alan Slash, Johnny and Margaret's son, squatted on his heels by the fire. He had ridden in during the night.

"Daylight come to the swamp," he grinned.

The coffee had muscles and the world began to look better. Stratocumulus fragments straggled eastward under clear skies, and tendrils of upslope fog stirred from the mountain. The beaver had repaired a dam during the night: the creek had fallen. Small trout were rising, and a weasel with ragged 79 patches of winter-white on his chocolate coat ran across a log. Soon he would be an ermine. When I squeaked like a terrified mouse he came to within a few feet. I glassed the lake below: two moose along the shore; the usual pair of loons; and trout rises glistening in the sun.

I helped Alan throw a squaw-hitch on his pack horse, then mounted the buckskin and, with Sack, continued west ahead of the others, glad to be on horseback because I could approach wildlife easier and have a better view. Song birds were all around me. Pine grosbeaks, crossbills, and pine siskins; juncos, chickadees, finches; nuthatches, kinglets, wrens; warblers, waxwings, tanagers. A pileated woodpecker gave his jungle-like call and flashed his scarlet crest through the trees. It is unusual to find this hermit anywhere but in the solitudes of ancient timber stands. He is a valuable member of the community because he creates nesting sites for other birds, and constantly hunts the larvae of wood-boring beetles. We rode past several deer. Bucks, sleek and fat and tame. I dismounted to examine a grizzly track and discovered a fresh wolf track. Sack said he didn't think much of the wolf.

Illusive, this brilliance of September, when cold air first flows over the southern slopes to bring night frosts to the valleys. Sensitized air ripples detail, each bird and leaf, into sharper focus, an interlude too soon over when, like the sensitive artist's hidden work, all is finally unveiled. Scarlet maples loosed purple glances; legs tucked in and golden heads together, poplars chattered; birch with creamy skins, and aspens' powdered trunks. Sunlight burst through a hidden pocket and the fireweed was like tracked-in confetti on a green carpet. We travelled through leaving little sign of our passing.

A black bear with three cubs crossed the trail and we galloped through the trees after them. All blueberry fat. The cubs soon scrambled up a poplar while their mother, who was decidedly unhappy at our rude interruption, circled about and woofed frustrated threats. One comic climbed to the top of the tree and swayed so much that he nearly fell off.

Black bears climb trees for the same reasons small boys climb trees. And to avoid a grizzly. They climb by gripping the sides of a tree; a cougar climbs cat-fashion up the face. Cougars have four claws on each foot, and large dewclaws on

80

the fronts; bears have five and no dewclaws. Grizzly cubs do
climb trees—I have watched them—but they are not so
ideally equipped as the blacks and, more serious by nature,
don't climb habitually. I have also known large black bears
unable to climb.

Adult grizzlies don't normally climb because of their
weight and long front claws, but I did once shoot one from a
tree. An adult female weighing 350 pounds. She was thin,
and the tree easy to climb. Three hounds were also on her
tail. This bear had been taking livestock and had several
infirmities: a .30-caliber bullet in a hip joint; claws twisted
and broken and several badly fractured toes; teeth badly
worn with three decayed molars and two splintered canines; a
large bald spot on her rump, and some skin disease. She was
the general color of an old haystack.

The breeze now carried the undulating crescendo of
Chinee Falls and I dismounted at a trickle and prepared a
fire. Slim and Charlie would appreciate some coffee. Besides,
Slim would likely want to ride for awhile.

The best approach to Dry Lake and the trail to Poplar
Mountain is by Kluskus Crossing, on the Euchiniko River
about four miles below Titetown Lake. The Poplar Mountain section of the Grease Trail can be maneuvered by four-
wheel-drive vehicles; at least to Kluskoil and, if dry, to Pan
Meadow Crossing, and to Trudeau's fishing and hunting
camp on the lower end of Euchiniko Lakes. Rainfall governs
road conditions, and between Kluskoil and Euchiniko Lakes
are some of the finest quagmires I have yet seen anywhere.
This "fair" wagon road is really merely rugged jeep trail,
receiving no maintenance other than what is provided by its
feverish travellers. Defectors from the cities leave it in an ever
more delightful state of wreckage. I prefer to relax in
Charlie's Bennett Buggy, the Bentley of the Blackwater, with
its pneumatic tires and all. Sort of amphibious too.

The first ford across the upper Blackwater, at Pan
Meadow Crossing, is ten miles west of Kluskoil and a couple
of miles east of Euchiniko Lakes. This crossing is extremely
dangerous in the spring, and several riders and mounts have
nearly met their ends here. Some likely have. One must use
discretion when attempting it, especially when the water is
high, or seems to be. Following a swim and a consultation

with his superior, Paul Krestenuk once erected a gauge-staff, to indicate the safe water level for saddle horse or wagon, but this Nazko-style instrument has long since disintegrated. Little Charlie tests the ford by saddle horse first because river channels and fords are constantly changing. Being a wide crossing of about one hundred yards, though, by mid-summer it usually only runs about two feet deep and with its solid bottom of gravel and medium-sized boulders is perfectly safe. At that time Little Charlie herds the wagon across without difficulty, but still not simply.

On the south bank a good horse trail or fair wagon road leads to Kluskus village, where in 1793 there were "two houses that occupied a most delightful situation," to Kusyuko Falls, and Tsacha Lake, Ulkatcho, and Dean River, by the Grease Trail. From Kluskus one can return to Nazko by way of the Baezaeko Trail to complete a short circle trip. The village name, Kluskus, means "half a whitefish-type fish," in Indian legend a magical fish with a large, fat body and a small, round mouth.

Should the Blackwater be surging, the sensible course is to continue west on the trail along the north bank for about three miles and get myself invited to dinner at Bunch Trudeau's—the best cook in the country, as well as a licensed guide who teaches riding and horse-sense to any youngsters who may be along. Guests usually fly in from Quesnel with float-equipped bush aircraft. In autumn, thousands of geese congregate on Euchiniko Lakes, and each fall Bunch counts sixty to eighty of British Columbia's few remaining trumpeter swans. The swans are among the last birds to migrate farther south or west, and stay until the last of the lake is frozen over. Some trumpeters, some Canada geese, and some mallards, remain to feed in the fast water and rapids all winter. There are plenty of five-pound trout here and in nearby lakes, and fifteen-pound char and Dolly Varden. One char from the upper lake weighed forty pounds.

The trail skirts the north shore of lower Euchiniko Lake, in a cradle of green and golden hills, to the west end where one can cross to the south bank at Jerryboy Crossing, also called Dead Horse Crossing, or Klay-na-stl-klee—"don't cross with saddle horse." This place has a mysterious undertow. And a terrible one. Many horses have drowned here, as well

as four people that I know of, all experienced riders. Bunch
has tacked up a warning notice for she too has seen the river
turn a saddle horse upside down. I once foolishly put a horse
in here from the south bank. He submerged like a hippo-
potamus, turned end over end and left me on my own.
Fortunately I had loosened the cinch and had removed his
bridle and my boots, and fortunately he was a good swimmer.
The less foolish Kluskus Indians keep a raft here, one large
enough to carry a wagon. The team goes next trip.

Nearly three miles farther upstream, just above Kluskus
River, is Sandyman Crossing or Shoo-an-schick—"spruce
trees grow to the water." Here Mackenzie made his first
crossing of the Blackwater "on a small raft." There is no raft
here now. Most often, if not always, the river is swimming
water for a horse. Not too clearly marked, though, and hard
to find from the north bank.

Six miles upriver is Ridge Crossing or Na-ta-ta-tee. Actually there are two crossings here: the upper one, to which the
trail from Kluskus church leads, is not safe during high
water; the other, about 300 yards downstream, is the only
ford which can be crossed by saddle horse with complete
safety at any time of the year. The last ford in this stretch is
Messue Crossing, at the upper end of Euchiniko Lakes and
below Kusyuko Falls. The Messue Indian band, a branch of
the Kluskus tribe located on Tatelkuz Lake, use it when
riding to Kluskus or Anahim Lake. Their north trail winds
up on the Kenney Dam road.

The upper lake of the Euchiniko Lakes chain is known
locally as Kloo-kah-nee-wa-a lake with a narrow ridge of
land circling out into it. The two distinct lakes in this chain
should each have a name. Kloo-kah-nee-wa, about five air-
miles long, is separated by a seven-mile stretch, more river
than lake, from six-mile Euchiniko Lake, which is dotted
with little islands. Both are narrow, probably averaging a
half-mile in width.

Swamps are the catch basins for the watershed and to cross
one of these I can usually go along a beaver dam. I am a
swamp wanderer, I like swamps, wet wild meadows, and
marshes. They interest me, and if there's one around I'll find
it, especially in spring. In Blackwater there are plateau, sub-
alpine, and divide swamps. Some are quite dry and others
very wet; some sweet-smelling and some stinking; some sugar 83

cane and rip-gut; some bog birch and mountain alder; all
strewn over the land in magnificent disorder. Most Blackwater swamps and meadows have rocky bottoms under the
humis, mud, and debris. A few have bog-holes that trap and
drown moose. From some swamps, the mosquitos can drive
anyone away.

Trickles of snowmelt and rainwater seep from the swamp
sponge to the rivers during freezeup, and once more beavers
are on the tiny trickles, reconstructing ancient flood control
dams which have been in disrepair since the old fur-traders
and trappers exterminated the original builders. Once more
beavers are forming shallow ponds or lakes rich in nutrients,
and creating suitable habitat for wildlife species from moose
to muskrats. Fish meander in and become residents; ducks
and geese and a pair of loons nest; the beaver channels ring
with bird songs. Otters and mink and muskrat establish
homes. Moose feed in swamps; water snakes and frogs and
aquatic insects thrive in them; bear dig roots along the shores
and eat the grasses; caribou, wolves, coyotes, stray cougar
and fur-bearers visit them. Each swamp teems with life, and
becomes a spruce-ringed oasis in the pines. Man can see little
good in this waste; these untidy swamps and marshes hinder
him and challenge him. He kills the beaver and drains the
swamp in order to grow grass to fatten cattle. Sometimes, on
purpose or accidentally, he burns what was once a swamp
and finds to his horror that the old beaver dam now encircles
a rocky nothing.

Packing horses every day can become a chore. A light
wagon simplifies moving and, with his, Charlie can trek
thirty miles a day without effort. And his horses are versatile:
they can be ridden, packed, or driven. We can therefore leave
the wagon and still be mobile if the road peters out. On a long
trip we take extra mounts, because the small mountain-bred
draft animals are not the most comfortable to ride. Besides,
most Indians train their saddle horses to jog-trot, to do the
Indian jig, an exceedingly uncomfortable gait except on long-
backed animals. A rider takes a few days to smooth out these
small fellows.

Charlie is an easy person to travel with because he uses his
head. He is a social being though, and when a tribal sing-song
84 with drum beats, ululations and kiiying, sounds far into the

night–a pleasant but rather sad song–he sometimes disappears, but with great tact.

He is not famous for his conversation, but when he has something to say we listen to his thoughts and learn from his experience. He can predict the actions of wildlife with amazing accuracy, but hunts strictly for food or fur. When he kills he kills as efficiently as possible, and by expending as little ammunition as he can. He stalks his game and can never understand why I shot birds one at a time, on the wing.

Returning form the west country, he and I, we had camped overnight at Dry Lake. The many pot-hole lakes and basins held lots of water that year, water and birds, and no hunters. The clatter of hundreds of geese and ducks greeted the dawn, some so tame they landed on the pond in front of the tent.

Charlie wasn't in camp when I awakened. The horses were hobbled out, but weren't within hearing and he'd gone looking for them. Finally, about mid-morning, he came in riding one and leading the others, thoroughly soaked from a heavy dew on the long walk he had had, and a long walk is something no horse-wrangler likes.

"Knot-headed crow-baits," he complained. "Lotsa feed this place. Why they go so far?"

He examined the birds I had hung up after having killed them so easily before I had had breakfast. Without comment, he then took six shot shells and my gun, and returned with six mallards and a Canada goose. He handed me back four shells. He had ground-swatted the flock of ducks and probably stalked the goose and got it by ground-swatting too.

Chapter Ten

Bear
Country

"Do I look very pale?"
Through the Looking-Glass
Lewis Carroll

Under Charlie's guidance the horses plodded along; they appeared to be in no hurry but were making good time. Sadsack scouted the trail ahead and tracked kangaroo mice through the grass. The sun was warm and I could easily have fallen asleep but I put the binoculars to good use on coyotes and hawks, and on anything else that was around and enjoyed the scenery.

"One time Francis Kassam, Bello Paul and Felix have lotsa grizzly trouble this place," said Charlie. "Francis killed big one. Hid behind that tree with 25.20 until bear come close. Shoot'm between the eyes." With a 25.20, I thought, I'd have been up that tree, not hiding behind it. "Bad time for grizzly then," continued Charlie. "They kill plenty cattle. Bad bunch come in here. Make it tough for everybody." 87

Having met some of these "grizzled and horrible" bears, as Alexander Mackenzie described them, I had to agree with Charlie. For many years grizzlies were only a confusing array of sub-species, but since 1953 the North American mainland population has been defined as one, *Ursus arctos horribilis,* pending systematic revision which will unlikely be made because almost everywhere the grizzly is an endangered species. Sub-species certainly do exist, but there is considerable overlapping of territories although grizzlies, generally, do not wander great distances. Some individuals do, and the minor invasion Charlie mentioned had probably come because the bear had been displaced elsewhere. Many homeless grizzlies retreated to Poplar Mountain and the upper Euchiniko when the Kenney Dam was being constructed.

In the Blackwater, a particular bear seldom kills more than once in a given locale; usually a large male, he is returning to a Coast Mountain salmon-spawning stream following a visit of unknown duration to the interior mountains. His course can be plotted across the country although admittedly the plotting lacks scientific proof, since it is based only on track or appearance. As the country is settled, his journeys between ranges become less frequent. Research and tagging could help to manage these bears and to ensure their future survival.

Grizzlies vary in color and build. Shades of brown, red, honey; some nearly black and some nearly white. Most have silvered head and withers, or silver pelage over most of the body, with darker legs. Many are two-tone: deep brown undertones and blonde on top, and change color somewhat with the seasons. One I examined was white, all white, with black feet and a few dark streaks on his face and neck. I've seen several near-white ones. On a snowfield, a sow and two yearling cubs all appeared cream-colored against the snow and wore black, knee-length boots. Some bears are long and lean, like polar bears; some are blocky. Head shapes also vary. Coast grizzlies are, on the average, larger than interior grizzlies.

British Columbia has many places in which to secure a good trophy and the Blackwater is not the best, although the upper watershed has a good population and some very big
ones. I have hunted all I ever intend to hunt, but still enjoy

watching them. When in their bailiwick for any reason,
though, a man can find himself having to move out quickly.
Associating with grizzlies is not recommended for anyone
with a heart condition. As one old Coast Indian remarked to
Charlie and me when we were enquiring about trails,
"Grizzly white man's bear. No good for people!"

These bears always look fierce, but are true furies when
wounded. When a grizzly charges, and occasionally he does
charge, a man requires a cool head to get out without killing
the bear, and a grizzly may charge for several reasons: he is
curious and wants a better look at you; he is bluffing and for
some reason is trying to put the run on you; or he's in dead
earnest. A serious bear will be roaring when he charges, but I
have also met roaring bluffers.

We are inclined to shoot too quickly. Several bears have
charged to within thirty feet of me, stood up, then dropped to
the ground and ambled away. I once in heavy timber surprised a female and her two small cubs and she immediately
charged to about twenty feet, stood up, and roared. I tried
not to panic–difficult when a grizzly is that close–and I
roared too, backed up, and then turned and walked away.
She seemed satisfied for she had not lost prestige. We met
again later on the river flats, but having already dealt with me
she paid me scant attention.

Twice I have blundered onto bears who have been snooz-
ing near their kill and who have awakened and charged me.
Favorite places are near lakeshores, meadows, or in the
bordering timber. After the first feast the bear sometimes
covers the kill with brush and debris in the manner of a
cougar. And they are very possessive and jealous of that kill
which could be a moose, caribou, black bear, a sick or
crippled animal, or winter-killed game, or a prime steer killed
with little effort and carried a considerable distance. Or the
kill might be a hunter's own big game. Hunters have killed
their moose in the evening, returned for it the following
morning, and have met a charging grizzly to whom the kill is
manna from bear heaven, and who now regards it as his own.

A visiting countess and her guide hung a quartered caribou
in a trapping cabin meathouse and, on returning the following morning for some breakfast liver, faced a silvertip who
had taken possession. The countess, who packed her 6.5

everywhere, calmly stepped to one side and killed him. She
had come for a trophy anyway, and got herself a good one.

By nature, bears seem to be as individualistic as people: some of them plain mean or neurotic, but most of them easy to get along with. Most will head the other way as fast as possible, even when met head on. Most of them, though, are exceedingly curious: they forever want to learn who and what you are. The have no enemies but man and other grizzlies, and need not pussyfoot about like most animals who wish to enjoy a long life. Some of them run, sometimes for no apparent reason; one loping through my camp one time ran slam into my clothesline, scattered the pots and pans, and did not look in any direction but straight ahead. Nothing seemed to be chasing him, but he went through the camp as though he had a swarm of hornets after him. Bears are also good swimmers. I watched one chug over a mile across a lake on some mysterious business and not even stop to catch his breath before starting up the mountain. Most seem to have poor eyesight or myopic vision, and depend largely on their keen powers of scent and hearing, but they will spot a quick move even at considerable distance. Many knowledgeable prospectors rattle pebbles in a tin can as they're walking along the trail to avoid surprising the bear, and when travelling through bear country Indian familes do a lot of talking and laughing; they keep up a chatter which can be heard for miles. Whistling in the dark. Conversely, game guides dispense with horse bells while hunting grizzlies. When slipping around quietly and downwind, to a grizzly a man is a sneaky-looking character. Personally I let him have a good sniff of me, because to him a sniff is as good as a look, and because usually a bear which scents a man is quickly on his way to the next mountain range.

Bears can cause so many anxious moments on a pack trip that sometimes you feel that the bear is *trying* to make trouble. They run back and forth across the trail, ahead and behind, but will eventually stand to one side within thirty feet of the trail and, head weaving, watch a rider go past. I ignore them—with my saddle-gun out. I've ridden several miles through a "gauntlet" of very big bears and emerged a wreck even though they never once roared or charged. Happiness is

having a good rifle.

Following a wounded grizzly can really be dangerous. In thick country game guides sometimes decline the honor, but tracking him down to finish him off is only humane and sportsmanlike. It is also wise, for if the bear does recuperate he becomes a potentially cranky hazard, and if he is permanently crippled he might start taking domestic animals for food. Ranchers may then, unfortunately, kill several innocent bears, and unfairly blame the species generally. In fact, some ranchers and cowpokes and hunters shoot at every bear they see and often with inferior firearms and at all ranges. Some Indians do the same.

In spite of his great bulk the grizzly is like a cat in the woods. And he is intelligent. When wounded and in sight he'll roar like a bull; hidden in timber or brush, unless the wound has affected his thinking, he will become as quiet as a mouse. He will allow you to follow him on his track, but will lie concealed behind a log or rock in order to attack from the rear at the opportune moment. He will die hard then. You will think your bullets are only making him bleed a little more quickly. When I shoot, I shoot to kill, for when he is wounded he's twice as difficult to finish off.

Around October 25 of a fairly open fall, I was visiting a ranch; not really a hunt, more of a fishing trip, although I thought I might climb to the goat country. The moose had finished the rut and most of the mature bulls had moved higher into the mountains until deep winter snows would bring them down again. Two friends of mine were hunting moose with their friend Jack from the big city. Derrik and Abbey had stalked to within sight of moose before, but Jack was a skier and mountain climber on his first hunting trip.

"I'm certain Abbey is stalking me," Jack confided. "Will you go moose hunting with me and show me how?"

I'm probably the worst possible moose hunting partner: invariably I get side-tracked and forget what I'm supposed to be doing. In addition, my hunting instinct seems to evaporate when I'm with someone else. What is more, I find no pleasure in hunting or killing moose, and prefer the prime meat of a bull killed in August. Although I'm lucky–I see a lot of them. But Jack handled his rifle carefully, the first thing I notice, and I agreed.

I started him off right by sighting in his new rifle, and soon

he was hitting the apple box every time—even with his thick
glasses he has poor eyesight. Early next morning we rode
south, towards a 6,900-foot mountain. We hunted some
sloughs and swamp-meadows but could only find cows and
calves, and when we examined some moose beds Jack suggested that we stick around and bushwhack them at bed time.
I decided his idea might have merit. In the afternoon we
picketed the horses and hunted a chain of willow-bordered
meadows at about 4,900 feet. The lodgepole pine forest and
thick fingers of Engelmann spruce ran back from the
meadows. A moosey place with plenty of fresh sign.

A deadfall broke heavily about fifty yards to our south.
Sounds of an animal running. Peering under the branches,
through the pine trunks, I could see nothing. The noise didn't
sound like a trotting moose. Jack had heard nothing; I asked
him.

Minutes later, when we were just well into a spruce thicket,
a number of grizzlies came charging, and when a number of
grizzlies charge simultaneously, and bloodshed is unavoidable, stop the leader. Unfortunate if you do not want to kill,
but sometimes necessary because the oddball might be
irritable, for a variety of reasons, or be a bear who has had
unhappy experiences with man.

Two were yearlings and two adults, one a very large silver-
tip. I had only three cartridges in the Mannlicher, and regretted not replacing the two I had fired at a coyote early that
morning. I never carry a cartridge in the chamber unless on a
stalk, but now for the first time I carried a half-empty rifle. I
was caught standing in a slight depression, Jack on a hillock
behind. They were about thirty feet away when we first saw
them and they had chosen the place. "Don't shoot!" I
yelled, not wanting any wounded grizzlies to hunt down.

Roaring like a locomotive, the largest bear kept running
towards us and fifteen feet away stood up. The one I put over
his head must have nearly parted his hair and almost
deafened him. The others circled around. The big leader kept
coming. Too close. I shot him in the top of the chest, just
below the neck. The fur flew. The bullet knocked him flat.
Up in a flash, still coming, as though not hit at all. Again I
knocked him flat. And was out of ammunition.

92   I reached around for Jack's rifle and threw open the bolt.

No cartridges. He had been hunting with an empty rifle or had unconsciously ejected them. Meanwhile, the shocked bear got up drunkenly, shuddered, and was into the timber. The others left with him as I thought they would.

For a few long minutes we stood discussing the facts of life pertaining to tracking wounded grizzlies while giving the bear time to die, or for the wounds to take effect, and for us to collect our wits.

"I'll be tracking," I advised Jack, who actually seemed to enjoy the prospect of the hunt and perhaps being able to stop a charging grizzly. "He'll be lying dead within two hundred yards. But do all the looking you can and watch the back-trail! If he's alive, he'll jump us in a thicket. If you see him, start shooting, and don't stop until he's down."

From a great heap of steaming dung, which indicated that he was hard hit, we trailed the few blood spots for about four hundred yards. Then slowly. It was a bad place: silver-grey lichen-covered boulders littered the thickly wooded flat. The bear seemed to have gone into thin air. We circled around and hunted until dark when I decided that this was no place to be, that we had lost the tracks anyway, and we returned to the ranch. The following morning we found where the others had bedded down, but found no further sign of the wounded one. He probably died close to the scene, and we would have found him quickly had Sadsack been along.

Only by good fortune were we safe; he had not kept coming. The action had been over in seconds, we had had no time to climb a tree, and I could not have reloaded in time. I shouldn't have been hunting with only three cartridges in the .270, with cartridges having light, fast handloads, good enough for killing moose or goat but unsuited for big bears at close range. I am not impressed with the killing capability of the .270-caliber in any case. Besides, I knew full well that I had heard a large bear running after he had cracked the downfall, and I should have been prepared. Nor should we have entered a thicket as quickly as we did. Jack stood directly behind me and a shot from his 30.06 would have deafened me. I had no time to explain, and what I did automatically he had to think over.

Later, we hunted in snow higher up the mountain. Bull moose were numerous and several grizzlies had been tracking

them in search of an easy kill. Undoubtedly these bears had
spent the fall fishing salmon and steelhead spawning-streams
in the lower coastal valleys, and were then drifting back into
the uplands to prepare for denning-in in about two weeks.

A good grizzly population depends upon large stands of
mature timber and when the timber is taken from an area the
grizzlies all but disappear. But tracking grizzlies through
dense forests is about the spookiest of bear-watching. Among
large trees one feels small anyway: the ghosts sway bearded
lichens, and branches squeak in the heavy silence; a deep
carpet of moss and lichens buries sound; visibility is often
limited to a few feet and it's semi-dark; the trees give an
occasional moan. The bruins trail each other, one treading
in the other's track in the manner of cougars, until over cen-
turies they have worn long, broad indentations through the
forest. In their beds, where they do a lot of sleeping during
the days, there are long brown hairs with silver tips. Some
beds are still warm. There must be ten grizzlies within a
three-mile radius. I have seen them standing up and staring
from fifty feet, silent and magnificent. A day usually passes
quickly, but at those times it stands still. When tracking
through a dusting of snow I've known that I've been the
tracker being tracked.

I have not surprised many grizzlies because they have very
sensitive hearing, but my hair has stood on end several times.
One day when skulking along I came to a large downfall,
jumped on the trunk, and a fellow in a grey fur coat rose at
my feet. A three-year-old, weighing about 400 pounds. He
ran for fifty feet, stood up and growled as though he had a
hole in his exhaust manifold. I had taken root, and quietly
advised him that the trees were too big for me to climb and
that he should go find his mother. He was too big to have one,
but dropped to the ground and ran off anyway. He had been
chewing on a moose leg in his bed under the downfall.

As with black bears, grizzly young are normally born in
alternate years but black bears raise larger families. Three
new cubs are quite usual with grizzlies, but often only one
remains by the second year. But juvenile mortality is likely no
higher than in many other species. Mother and cubs den
together the first winter, but should mother have an un-
94 planned family increase around the end of February the

earlier cubs could find themselves out in a cold world. For this perfectly natural reason, yearling bears, black or grizzly, may occasionally be found rambling March snows searching for new homes. Otherwise the cubs stay with mother through the second summer. A grizzly does not have an easy life: the males fight a great deal, especially during mating season in early summer; and I've heard fierce battles at their kills.

We think of grizzlies as being alpine dwellers, but historically they roamed most of the Interior Plateau above 3,500 feet elevation. They feed there all summer, and then drift to salmon streams. In the immense stands of prime spruce laced with bear trails they have wallowing holes and small lakes for swimming; streams of spawning trout and suckers; openings and sidehills for an abundance of berries.

The ecology is being drastically altered as many of the spruce stands are being harvested. The plateau is now crisscrossed with logging roads, and pretty little lakes serve for log dumps with the usual result. Polluted water and no fish. In a few years all the big timber will be gone and meanwhile the logging and pulp companies eye our provincial parks.

Metabolism functioning on the stored fats from a bountiful summer, Blackwater bears hibernate about the first week of November, depending upon when the true hibernal wind trips their thermostat. I have seen bears out on November 15, when small lakes were frozen over and several inches of snow covered the ground, but these bears were sleepy and close to their dens. When the white wind arrived not a bear track could I find. I did, though, discover an adult black bear out sleep-walking in February, the only time I've seen an adult out during mid-winter in interior British Columbia.

The Continental Arctic air mass, with a Polar frontal system far south of its usual boundary, had been wedged over Central British Columbia for days. The mercury was hovering around 50° below and the valley was shrouded in ice fog. Everyone was indoors stoking fires, making bets, and curing hangovers. The office heating system wasn't built for this cold, so I therefore decided to close shop and go hunting for a roving wolf pack that checked in regularly from December through March—just to find out what they were up to. A man must adapt, respond, and defer to nature.

I snowshoed about five miles and, dressed in woolen long-

johns, goosedown underwear, eiderdown socks and native
mukluks, didn't feel any colder than on some other days. A
large track, coming from the direction of a stand of cottonwood trees to the south, joined the trail; it then continued
north toward the canyons and steep bluffs where I'd tracked
cougar. A few hundred yards farther on it rejoined the trail.

"Some poor old cayuse," I thought, "hunting a place to
paw some grass."

Of the four feet of snow, the top eighteen inches were
powder-dry and fluffy. The track or, more correctly, trail
through the snow didn't seem to be exactly right for a horse. I
removed a mitten and felt the hidden outline. A bear, out
wandering in this weather! Perhaps a grizzly. He continued
west on the trail for half-a-mile, headed south once more, and
I more or less forgot him.

I never did see the wolves, but I did notice that the bear had
not recrossed the trail and I felt that I should find out what
he was up to. I checked the 6.5 and put a cartridge in the
chamber. I hadn't travelled far when I found where he had
gone to a fair amount of work to start to dig a den in a gravel
hill, but somehow wasn't satisfied and accordingly continued
on his way. Another two hundred yards and the same thing.
As I slipped farther along I saw gravel and dirt flying up onto
the snow.

I couldn't see him properly until I was within fifteen feet of
him. His thin rump was visible; the debris which flew past on
one side and then the other he cast out sluggishly. I sidewalk-
superintended for a few minutes and actually saw him shiver
several times before I spoke: "You don't look at all well." He
slowly shuffled around, poked his head up to see where this
observation came from, and I shot him between his dull and
sleepy eyes. I should really have waited until he had come out
of the excavation for I had to remove my belt, put it around
his neck and finally heave him out. By this time it was nearing
three o'clock and getting cold again. I built a roaring fire and
boiled a pot of tea, and then removed his hide.

He was a large black bear with a prime pelt, but he hadn't
a spare ounce of fat on him. The previous summer had
produced a generally poor berry crop and the bears had been
trying to fatten on rose hips which are rich in vitamin C but
contain little of food value. This bear had not stored up

enough fat to keep him functioning during hibernation and
he would not have survived the three long months until
spring.

Conceivably he might have been able to eke out an existence along two nearby rivers: his nose may have led him to salmon carcasses, cattle or game remains, or whatever else ends up in rivers. But my intestinal autopsy showed he hadn't. In the lower intestine of a hibernating bear there is a "plug" mainly composed of grasses. Bears must purge themselves with roots immediately they emerge from hibernation. If they don't they are in trouble. Perhaps this explains why newly emerged bears are inclined to be short-tempered.

Chapter Eleven

Kluskoil

You boil it in sawdust: you salt it in glue:
You condense it with locusts and tape:
Still keeping one principal object in view—
To preserve its symmetrical shape.

"The Hunting of the Snark"
Lewis Carroll

Kluskoil Lake occupies a crescent-shaped depression averaging half-a-mile in width. From its discharge at mid-out-curve, the southwest arm of the lake is four miles long, and the southeast arm backs into the hills for two and a half miles. Islands jut from the lake and fingers of water run into rock-bottomed coves and spruce-forested peninsulas.

Slim had scouted out a pine-dotted aspen flat on the north shore. Hideout essentials, grazing and water and firewood, were handy. A family of black bears rambled the grassy slopes to the northwest. A flat-topped mountain dominated the south: Chine Bluff, a 4,300-foot volcanic cinder cone, its slopes rising gently from the lake for 1,400 feet. We pitched the tent, moved in our gear, and cooked lunch. Charlie hobbled the horses and turned them loose in the lush grass to the west.

99

The rumble of Chinee Falls drew us. We walked the half-mile, through open pine and spruce woods. A cinnamon-colored black bear reared up and woofed, dropped to all fours, and crashed away through the downfall at top speed. Plenty of bear sign here. This one had been grubbing in an ant-hill.

Many of the larger interior lakes were formed when glaciation deepened a trench and subsequently blocked the valley with glacial debris. No doubt such debris blocked it in post-glacial times, and then glacial meltwater and later the river cut a path through this material down to an erosion-resistant lava. As a result, a short, swift, outlet river, of fairly even depth, now flows north from the lake over a flat-lying lava bed. At the "falls" or downstream end, portions of the lava shelf have fractured off into immense blocks, and here the torrent thunders through a chute, into the pool below, and across a lower bed of lava littered with gigantic black rocks. It was not a straight fall of water as I had supposed.

The deep potholes pocking the lava beds are circular pools formed during flood, when the river eddies swirl rocks and abrasive sand in a circular scouring action. A red squirrel had fallen into one which was partly full of water, and he had drowned. Several Dolly Varden lay in the tail-end of the first pool. And some immense squawfish. In minutes we had wet our lines and caught several two to three-pound trout. The river was fast and they fought well. I continued downstream, along a game trail, and along banks thickly wooded with shade trees.

Beyond a brawling tributary I found another falls, or boulder-strewn rapid. The river now curved easterly through flat-lying lava flows and made very fishable water. The foam-flecked pool teemed with scrappy little one-to three-pound rainbows which seemed to spend more time in the air than in the water, and, because they would have the fly first, larger trout seemed impossible to catch.

Slim released a six-pounder which he thought from the color could have been a steelhead. These fish live in the spawning streams for their first two years of life and migrate seaward when six or seven inches long. When four years old they return to fresh water to spawn, and as spawning time nears they take on the coloring of the rainbow trout. Steelhead do not always die upon spawning, but return to the sea, and may return to spawn a second or even third time. For them, spawning is more leisurely than for Pacific salmon, and some runs live in the river system for several months before laying their eggs and returning to the sea as "kelts."

We decided to postpone further discovery and fish the lake for char, but when going past the small brook, I couldn't resist walking upstream a few steps and teasing the fly along the bubbly froth of a dark pool. Several trout leaped and missed, but when one grabbed I flipped him to the bank. He was in excellent condition but as dark as night, having probably come down from some beaver-dammed backwater. I plopped him into the main river: in a few weeks he would look as though he had always been there.

Most fishermen are acquainted with trout camouflage. Disguised to fit the play of current over multi-colored pebbles, the residents of a clear mountain stream are scarcely detectable. In a lake like Azure, in the Clearwater basin, for example, they mask themselves in a pale-blue sheen, the hue of the lake. Rainbows in the Stellako River in the Nechako basin are heavily spotted and brightly colored. At least, those are who manage to hatch to life in spite of the debris-smothered spawning beds, bank erosion, and stream bed scouring caused by "controlled" log-drives.

The Blackwater tribe with their rainbow stripes are generally more silver than the highly-colored Stellako fish: delicately spotted on the upper fins and tail, head and gill covers; transparent, pink-orange fins below, with black spots and small black X's on the steel-green upper half of the body. Sometimes, with the diffusive shadows along their rippled iridescence, and the wildness in their eyes, they seem too handsome to kill. The colors would fade with their life. They grow fast and plump and solid.

Much of this general area between the Coglistiko and the Kushya River headwaters, the area north of the Archies where several drainage systems originate, is one gigantic sponge, filled with space and solitude, but I've captured Blackwater trout in these most unlikely places. Trout from Blackwater lakes, which are rich in fresh water shrimp and plankton, have red-orange meat, while those from rivers and streams are pale pink. One from a muskeg pool weighed four

BLACKWATER RIVER pounds, had unusually vivid markings, a stomach that bulged with nymphs, and flesh that was firm and red, but on cooking him for Sadsack and sampling some myself, I found the meat to be swamp-flavored.

The muskeg area itself was several miles long, easily a mile wide, and contained several open pools. Ias center appeared to be rounded like an inverted saucer. I could detect no flow of water but there would have to be a trickle to the main drainage, the Kushya, which empties into the Blackwater above Kusyuko Falls and has at least two trout-filled lakes in its basin.

No glacial ice remains in the Blackwater basin; the tributary streams which flow from lakes high in nutrients account for the excellent fishing. In glaciated mountainous regions many lakes are deep, cold, and unproductive, their bottom food is sparse and difficult for fish to hunt, and their plankton resources low, and they support few trout. Sometimes they support only coarse fish. Tributary streams to such lakes are usually of glacial origin; they are usually cold and heavily charged with "rock flour" silt, which is pollution of the natural sort, one which seriously hampers spawning success, smothers bottom fauna, and reduces photosynthesis. These glacial streams usually have steep gradients, a high water velocity, and a high flushing rate; they are low in dissolved nutrients and their permeable gravel is coarse and constantly shifting.

To hatch successfully, trout eggs require a constant flow of reasonably clean, well-aerated water percolating through the spawning nest, to flush away metabolic wastes and to supply the necessary oxygen. Fine silt adheres to the eggs and encases them in a hard coating, blocks the metabolic exchange, and prevents the eggs from hatching. Newly emerged fry may also be suffocated by silt, but they become more tolerant as they become older.

Lake rainbows migrate to their spawning streams in late April, May, and early June, depending upon the fluctuations in water-temperature and in stream-flow. Streams receiving most of their flow from headwater lakes have a temperature rise from the winter low of near 32° F to around 40° F immediately after the thermal overturn of the lake in spring, or from about May 1 to 15. As temperatures and flow increase the spawning migration commences. Streams of glacial origin have temperatures ranging from 32° to 38° until early June and therefore have delayed spawning. The time required for trout eggs to hatch is also greatly affected by temperature. If the eggs receive a constant flow of 42° water they require sixty to seventy days to hatch; at higher temperatures development is faster.

Most eggs are laid and fertilized by June 1. Fry emergence commences around June 20 and is usually complete, in most streams, by July 20, but sometimes not until early August. The fry remain near the site for a short period, and usually migrate to the lake by late August. Some remain longer, or take up stream residence. June and July are usually high-water months in the glacial areas, and the eggs and small fry receive the full load of silt.

"How did Chinee Falls get its name, Charlie?" I asked.

"Tseenee. Indian name. Like plenty of big rocks at this place. Bad rapid along here. For long time nobody travel the river. People use spruce canoes at one time. Horses better if you want to go some place." The Carrier names for prominent landmarks in the watershed are interesting and graphic, but quite often defy translation. Some people make the mistake of thinking that the name of the falls comes from nearby Chine Bluff.

"Are you coming along for some lake fishing, Charlie?"

I rigged the trolling outfit, attached a heavy leader and large spoon to the lead-core line. We launched the canoe and paddled southwest until, by the lay of the hills, we thought we should be over a deep pocket. I lowered more than a hundred feet of line and we had travelled only a few more yards when the rod slowly bent. The lure must have hooked bottom. But it then gave somewhat. I felt a tug. Whatever I had hooked was alive.

Recovering line, I found no real fight, just pressure and weight. The fish took a deep run and the struggle started in earnest. He made several runs before I could bring him to the surface. When a char's grey-green length with pale-yellow splotches appeared, Slim netted him. "About twelve pounds," he estimated. "Keep him?"

"Catch us a smaller one for supper." Charlie thinks we are pretty crazy fishermen because we release most of the fish that we catch, although I've noticed that he too, on occasion, does the same and is even more gentle than we are.

Slim caught several more. Their lily-white bellies bulged with kokanee, and Charlie, who was scanning the shores with my binoculars, pointed to a bay where dimples flashed. "Little redfish good eating."

We paddled over. I put up a caribou hair dry-fly. Slim's resembled a Grizzly King. One fish rose to my cast but I missed the strike. Another came cautiously, struggled briefly, and I flipped him into the canoe. Bright silver-blue color, slender caudal peduncle, forked tail, small teeth, a dusting of black speckles, and firm: a kokanee, or "kickininee." We caught about twelve, each a plump miniature salmon of the lakes, ten or eleven inches in length.

There is in British Columbia no closed season for fishing in lakes and no bag-limit on kokanee, but the law prohibits disturbing or fishing kokanee in streams. Except when on a feeding spree in early summer, kokanee take a fly in somewhat the same delicate manner as Arctic grayling. Trout seem simple to hook after a session with these discriminating feeders.

The rich, orange-colored flesh is delicious prepared any way, but when immersed in brine and herbs overnight, then smoked slowly over genuine alder for about eight hours, they are especially delectable. They are fine also when salted down in a small wooden tub and later prepared like pickled herring or salmon. One can also drown them in wine for several days, clean and fillet later, and serve them with sour cream and dark rye bread.

Most sport fish in British Columbia belong to the salmonid family: the trout—rainbow and steelhead, cutthroat, and the artifically introduced brown—given the scientific name *Salmo;* the char—Dolly Varden, Great Lakes char, and the artificially introduced Eastern brook or speckled char—all called *Salvelinus;* and the five species of Pacific salmon, *Ornorhynchus.* Trout and char can spawn more than once, whereas Pacific salmon invariably die upon spawning. Our native trout spawn in spring, char and brown trout in late summer or autumn.

Kokanee or "landlocked sockeye salmon" enter their
spawning streams from lakes in mid-September through early

November. The reproductive instincts of each of the many races of kokanee governs the time of the spawning migration. On the Euchiniko they spawn in October, and when early November ice cakes whisper along other Blackwater tributaries. Three biologically distinct races have been identified in some lakes, and each race migrates to a separate spawning ground. Like their large sockeye relatives, returning from the sea to spawn, the bodies of male kokanee turn crimson while their heads remain green, and all die.

They sometimes use stream gravel deltas for spawning. Like most members of the salmonid family they prefer a moderate run of clear water around two to three feet a second, but broken by pools and flowing over riffles of gravel, much of it pea and marble size, stabilized by substrate two to six inches in diameter. And they prefer their water to be free of silt, large amounts of fine sand, sawdust, chips, logging debris and bark, chemical wastes, raw or treated sewage, and the millions of tons of other waste materials entering our rivers each day.

The alevins emerge from the spawning nest, or redd, in late winter or early spring, and the fry immediately drop downstream to their home lake. They take up residence in deep water, and there they remain for the first two to three years of life. Plankton and other small animal life is almost their exclusive food, strained from the water by means of numerous slender gill rakers which are more efficient for collecting plankton than those of trout.

When approaching four years of age, the average age of maturity, the kokanee spread throughout the lake and become an important source of food for large rainbow trout and fly-fishermen. Both rainbows and these fishermen prefer relatively shallow waters of the lake; thus kokanee are spatially separated from trout and fly-casters until this time.

The four-year-old fish are now six to twelve inches in most lakes, much larger in others. The trout, therefore, must be sufficiently large to utilize this high-energy food. Lake char on the other hand commonly inhabit very deep water. Kokanee are important forage fish for nearly all age groups of char which also prey on sculpins, or bullheads, dace or shiners, peamouth chub, young suckers, squawfish and whitefish. When still comparatively small themselves, and having much larger mouths than trout, char can prey on fairly large fish.

Few lakes will support twenty- to thirty-pound rainbow trout—Kootenay, Quesnel, Stewart and Babine, to name four of renown. A productive lake that has been barren of fish will often produce whoppers three or four years after first being stocked, as will a winter-killed lake that again comes on, but size levels off in the competition for food. Large rainbow trout have genetic differences developed through successive generations, and belong to races separate from the general trout population of a lake. As a result, for successful control, these rainbows should be considered separately.

Large rainbow trout become totally dependent for their food supply on kokanee. Should the cyclic kokanee runs be lost through hydro dams flooding out and silting over spawning beds, affecting stream-flow, water temperatures, and oxygen content, or through insecticides wiping out the return run, the large trout lose their food supply, decrease in numbers, and become extinct. Dam destruction can sometimes be alleviated temporarily by installing an artificial spawning channel for the kokanee, but such biological truths come slowly, and are even more slowly accepted.

Of passing interest is the presence in some lakes of a sockeye salmon sub-form, of "residuals," the non-anadromous offspring of anadromous sockeye. Or, more simply, a young sockeye that for some reason or another does not make the journey to the sea. As a residual, he differs only morphologically from kokanee, and therefore is indistinguishable to most people.

Behavioral differences offer at present the only clue to true identity. Most sockeye smolts migrate seaward during the second or third summer after hatching, and most return to their birthplace when four years of age. Pacific salmon generally and sockeye in particular—and therefore residuals too—return to their natal streams to spawn. Kokanee also have this homing instinct, but our "sockeye dropout" was likely hatched on a spawning bed in a main waterway, whereas the kokanee usually spawn in more obscure tributaries. The two forms, kokanee and residuals, seldom meet on the spawning beds. The few melancholy "kokanee" observed

on sockeye spawning beds are quite probably really residuals *Kluskoil*
which have returned to the clan. The mysterious little
kokanee, he takes little from life and gives life to all, including char.

Great Lakes char, commonly called lake trout or simply
char, grow to sixty pounds in some British Columbia lakes
and attain a great age for fishes, ten years being common.
They construct spawning nests near sub-surface springs, but
generally spawn on reefs, deltas and, occasionally, in the
relatively deep slow-moving areas of adjoining river. Mature
char prey largely on kokanee, and kokanee move to different
levels in search of their main food, a rib-sticking protein with
daily vertical migrations and a seasonal abundance at certain
levels, plankton. Plankton lies in pockets in many large lakes
because of the thermal structure of the lake. The isotherms
take pronounced dips and sometimes warmer water lies at
greater depths.

Good fishing requires locating the deep places, noting by
the amount of line used the depth at which the fish was taken
and not straying too far from that spot. Most guides know
where char are to be found at different seasons, and at what
depth and take cross-bearings on landmarks. Indian paint-
ings on the shoreline cliffs sometimes tell of traditional char
holes, and of places where Indians captured char by mooching a kokanee through a hole in the ice. Mooching is a very
relaxing way to fish on a summer day, too, certainly more
interesting than trolling hardware. Because of my comparatively light tackle—an old double-handed salmon fly rod
with the tip cut down—and the close involvement of one's
senses—I like mooching next best to fly-fishing. I have used
this technique of strip casting a small kokanee on a long
leader and plenty of line, letting it sink and then working it in,
or something like this technique, to capture char, and occasionally at shallower depths to get even with a monster trout.

Sack greeted our return with tail-wagging and shaking.
Not to be left out, he had swam the outlet river, and had
taken a short-cut across two narrows, and around the south
shore to where we were fishing. No sooner had he arrived
when he had to start back. He swam the lake straight across.

We baked foil-wrapped char and enjoyed Chinee cocktails. Sunset drenched the shores, and tawny aspens changed to red aspens. An otter V'd the shimmering lake on his evening rounds. Well escorted, a young loon cruised bravely by, babbling an incredible tale to his parents who laughed as idiotically. A coyote answered their distress from farther up the shore, and in turn two others answered from different sectors. Discordant yelps and wild laughter: a yodeling chorus filled the darkening valley. We added to the frenetic bedlam when Sack hit an unacceptable note and his echo returned to brooding silence.

"People see lights on that mountain," said Charlie, nodding at the flat-topped profile to our south, Chine Bluff.

I thought a moment before asking what kind of lights.

"I dunno. People who stop this place see lights. At night." If Charlie said people saw lights, people saw lights. Maybe we'd see some tonight.

"On the slope, or on top?"

"Near mountain top. Long time ago this big stopping place. People not come much now. Little lake is in where that mountain split. Lotsa animal bones around the shore."

"Is the water poisoned?" I prompted.

He shrugged: "Lotsa bones." And lapsed into silence.

Southeast from Kluskoil, towards Fishpot Lake, there has been volcanic activity during some period of the post-pleistocene; eruptions of ash and cinders lie on glacial till. A small, steep-sided crater lake lies in a mountain southeast of Fishpot. Unmistakeably of this volcanic origin, Chine Bluff decorated the landscape. The pine and spruce-forested slopes looked easy to climb. No doubt the summit slopes would be covered in scree. Slim and I speculated on what might cause the lights and bones but Charlie did not join in. Certain regions with strange lava formations, huge dark rocks, dark waters and silence can produce a foreboding to people living in the shadow, and stories of strange lights and huge, wild, hairy men, or sasquatch, circulate periodically, usually toward spring. "Just squaw-talk," though, Charlie commented one time when an encampment was hysterical over the activities of one local sasquatch.

"We'll climb to the fissure sometime," said Slim. "I don't know of any poison water in the country, but we'll take some good stuff just in case. When you heading back to Nazko, Charlie?"

"Stop here to-morrow to rest horses," he explained. I said I'd like to look at the country to the north in the morning and asked if I might ride the buckskin.

"Sure. Okay. He's not tired."

Altocumulus banded the south horizon and the moon, near-full, shone clear. Charlie bedded down under the wagon, Slim went to a spruce, and I spread my tarp and goatskin beneath a tall aspen. A keen north-westerly chattered the never-still aspen leaves and carried the fragrance of pine. Horse bells chimed a grazing aria above the muted river. Two articulate horned owls hooted compromise during each other's intervals. I was tempted to stalk one close to camp by walking towards his hoots, but unrolled my eiderdown instead and crawled in.

The stars were still bright when Sack awakened me. He snuffed in the breeze, puffed out his jowls, blew out the wind and cursed. A mouse scampered over my foot and fled. Distant geese fell silent. Wind-shifted frogs took an intermission. Distance subdued a drawn out moan.

"Just a good old wolf, Sack." He gave me a look of disgust.

Chapter
Twelve

Blood Brothers

"Suppose he never commits the crime?"
said Alice.

Through the Looking-Glass
Lewis Carroll

Indian Legend supports the belief that wolves have always ranged the Blackwater. Wolf populations have declined or increased, however, in response to opportunities to gain food through the main prey species, elk, caribou, deer and, more recently, moose. Ideal conditions for an increase in wolves and other fur-bearers came when the number of moose which had invaded the winter ranges grew to wondrous proportions. A balance between wolves and their food supply is a population control of some sort, though people have difficulty in understanding and accepting that wolves cull out the weak and diseased, and thereby help to maintain populations of healthy, vigorous big game animals. Hunters crop some surplus game animals and, if regulated, might control population levels, but hunting does not replace the routine and constant culling through natural predation, although the two do overlap to some degree. Most hunters try to kill the first animal they see, and often leave it crippled; wolves search out the weaklings.

An examination of wolf kills discloses some of the weaknesses in the prey. Lung adhesions and massive obstruction by hydatid tapeworm cysts in the lungs slow them down; lumpjaw interferes with feeding; bone marrow fat depletion indicates extreme malnutrition from one cause or another. Most kills are calf moose with diseased or weakling mothers, or moose over the age of about nine years for these kills are easy kills. Only rarely do wolves take a prime animal that has no physical disability. The wolf is nature's helper; once an animal has outlived his usefulness it's into the larder with him. I don't begrudge the wolves this food.

I have studied wolf habits at every opportunity, but really know little about their private lives. I do know that they love to bug a coyote caught out on an open burn or lake: they circle, play with him, gradually close in, run him through the gauntlet, and reduce him to hamburger. I know that when they kill a moose they eat the nose immediately. Even if they eat little else, and then stockpile the kill for the future, they eat that wolf delicacy first. After that they go into the chest cavity and eat the lungs and liver, and follow by eating the more meaty pieces. I am also aware that a wolf probably has a keener nose than any other animal: he will beeline across the ice of a lake, suddenly stop and dig through several inches of snow and ice to reach a winter-killed fish which has been completely frozen in. One time I followed the fresh tracks of seven wolves to the remains of a medium-sized black bear the rascals had smelled and dug out of his cosy den. They had eaten him. It had been no contest. And wolves most emphatically and fortunately do not attack a human, but once I lost a dog who wasn't smart enough to outmaneuver them. A rabid individual would be an exception, but there is no record of rabies in British Columbia. I followed a pack of eighteen one night on a trail so firmly packed that I removed my snowshoes for a time. It was pitch black; wolves howled all around me; terrified cougar dogs tried to climb into my pockets. I wouldn't have missed the experience, but nothing 112 more exciting happened.

Most winter packs number six to eight; a family group. The largest pack of wolves I know of numbered twenty-four, at least two family groups, or a pack whose mating members had rejoined it. Hunting as a winter pack, wolves normally bring a moose down in two hundred yards or less. They favor running the quarry out onto the shore ice of a lake where the snow is often packed and where footing is better for themselves and more hazardous for the hoofed prey. Wolves do not always have an easy time however: when the snow is loose and deep they have difficulty catching up to the long-legged moose and, as I have seen from an aeroplane, flounder to a stop for an occasional rest. In timber though, the pack kills the chosen victim without difficulty.

I have many times seen a place where a pack of wolves has circled and annoyed a moose, tried him out or "tested" him. One April, in a mountainous, narrow valley, a place in a heavy snow belt where moose "yard," eight wolves just ahead of me had "tested" several of them. The wolves, in searching for an easy kill, had put the moose into a bad humor and I was forced to detour around some of them. A cow which was pregnant and with a yearling calf put me in the river with my snowshoes still on. A little later, in six feet of snow, I saw an ancient cow with a calf so small that his ears barely poked above the moose trail. Evidently he had arrived prematurely. This old cow and young calf would seem to have been lead-pipe cinches for wolves, but when I became too inquisitive she put the run on me and trampled Sack into the snow, as she had done the wolves before us.

A pack of wolves see many moose in their travels and choose the easy ones, the sick and infirm ones. Trained and observant people notice a sick animal easily: he stands and walks differently, he doesn't seem to be as keen as the others. It must be extremely simple for a wolf with animal intuition and experience to spot weaknesses when the pack travels a chain of lakes and rivers which is game wintering grounds. It travels many miles, sometimes hundreds, and usually takes about fourteen days to complete its circuit, even though it might remain in one area for several days.

Trappers who have shot several wolves have told me they have met a pack on a "meat drunk," a pack which has overeaten at a fresh kill and become stupified. I am skeptical.

For years I wandered the woods and jumped wolves from
fresh kills, and never yet encountered a drunken one.

But I have seen sexy wolves. Most shootings occur when
they are in season, during the first two weeks of February,
with peak activity just before St. Valentine's Day. Wolves
breed during the second or third year, and the mating pair
leave the pack for whelping purposes. The young are born
between April 1 and April 15, the gestation period being
about sixty-five days, and the pair remain together to raise
their young.

Finding a wolf den is easy; finding one in use for whelping
is not. By accident Old Joe discovered a den near one of his
hideouts, barricaded the entrance with logs and rocks as big
as he and his horse could move, and then left to get a shovel
to dig them out. "I sloped outa there as fast as I could go," he
reported, "but when I came back those wolfs had everything
torn to hell, and packed off the pups. They are sure smart."

The pups do not stay in the den any longer than absolutely
necessary, and they hunt together as a family until at least the
following December. The parents sometimes have difficulty
obtaining adequate food for their young and take anything
they can get. One pair killed about twenty sheep and took
three yearling steers from cow camps and ranches. This pair
would have been a problem when the cattle were turned out
on the range with their calves, although their parent pack,
which operated in much the same area, caused no trouble.

These two adults were of normal size: the male, weighing
106 pounds, measured sixty-nine inches long; the female,
weighing ninety-eight pounds, was sixty-two inches long. She
would have whelped ten pups, the largest number recorded in
northwestern North America to that time. The largest wolf
that I have myself weighed was a 123-pound male. Most
wolves that I have examined were juveniles, weighing eighty
to ninety pounds and had prime winter pelts. Most were black
or dark, fading gradually to silver underparts. In the Cariboo, about twenty per cent are grey, much like a coyote, and
as large as the black variation. One I caught in a cougar snare
was nearly all white, a beautiful fur.

Most old Indians are opposed to killing wolves. A Quesnel
114 Indian, very much a loner and one of the last of his tribe,

visited me at the office occasionally and we sometimes met in the woods. Our conversations were limited, for he didn't speak English well and my Carrier is far from good. One day I had pulled the pick-up into town and was gassing it up. Five or six wolf corpses lay in the back. My friend came by, shuffling along on an invisible pair of snowshoes, bucking his blizzard, as always. He saw me and smiled, then saw the wolves. Because of his anger, added to the communication problem, about all I could understand was "Those are my brothers you kill!" According to Indian mythology the spirit of the dead returned in a wolf, but only if the dead had been a good hunter. Old Johnny himself will surely return as a great old grey timber wolf.

Predator control is unnecessary except to protect domestic stock. The rare exception would be for the complete protection of re-introduced or endangered species of wildlife for a limited period of time. Wolves and other predators are the "public health" enforcers who benefit the entire wildlife community, and help maintain healthy ungulate herds. Most informed sportsmen know this, know how the wildlife community is structured, and how wolves, coyotes, foxes, cougars, bobcats, lynx, horned owls, hawks, eagles and ospreys add drama to the outdoor scene. Most sheep-herders, a few game guides, and some cattle ranchers, on the other hand, consider the only good wolf, coyote, cougar, or grizzly to be the one stretching his hide on the barn.

Since I wasn't doing much one winter, I lived with a friend's herd, and thus learned first hand some of the problems associated with ranching, learned just what made a cattle ranch tick. Although I was mistaken, I also thought it would be a good place to think—a satellite cow-camp located on a string of plateau meadows, several miles into the boonies from the main ranch.

My seventy-three pregnant ladies, and an ancient sway-back cayuse with ringbone and poor teeth, were not in the best of shape. In fact several were caved-in quite badly. There was wild hay to feed them, but it was rotten and frozen, and we had to bring in several tons of pellets, some crushed oats, a few bales of alfalfa, and fortified salt to boost the intake. I got them out of bed most mornings, and stuffed them twice a day.

Distributing the goodies would cause small stampedes: the cattle wrecked my sleigh, stepped on my toes, and spooked my horse.

Generally, they got into the damndest predicaments, but I learned that range cows have an obsession for protocol and live for the day they can climb to yet a higher rung on the social ladder. It's a constant fight to retain a hard-won position. The queen of this lost battalion was a mean and dangerous erotic, a large cow who took what she wanted. The others gave way or took a trouncing on the spot. She gave way to Blackie, my horse, or to me, but only because she knew we were her servants.

A calf elevates a cow's status. Premature calves, sired by a neighbor's "steer," arrived in early March. One was born dead, or didn't last his first night. The next calf took us all by surprise. I'd trailed his innocent-looking mother to a spruce thicket, found him with her, then carried him to the maternity ward behind the horse barn, where all the mothers-to-be gathered in a tight circle around the fence. Their intense and lengthy visit was full of jealousy, advice, and frustrated remarks. When the calf's mother moaned for him to come to nurse, a dead silence followed. The calf staggered to his feet from his bed of hay, and took his first brave steps toward her. Outburst of comment from the visitors! And I found I had been sitting on the corral for two hours.

Several weeks later, when I at least smelled like a cowpoke, I left my horse to mind the cows and went with Old Joe for a beer.

"How you like cattle ranching?" he asked.

"I don't love cows," I told him, but I also admitted that they're really as smart as horses and do decorate the landscape to some extent. By this time I had a pet marten, one remaining squirrel, two weasels, five camp-robbers, a pack-rat, several chickadees, a moose, a pigmy owl, but no mice or shrews. Coyotes yodelled nearly every evening and morning. I raised about three grouse for each mile I rode—an indication that grouse should be plentiful in the fall. The cows must have been feeling well because they scrapped a lot. There were always one or two in the hospital behind the horse barn.

"You'll get the feel," he said. "Cows are just like sheep only bigger and smarter and meaner. Give the sick ones a
116   shotta snoose. They'll be okay."

By 1946 the Wildlife Branch was forced to control wolves on most beef cattle ranges: the moose population explosion had created unusually ideal conditions for a steady increase in wolves, but when large-scale winter moose die-offs occurred a top-heavy wolf population remained. Heretofore, ranchers protected their interests as best they could, but few people knew how to catch wolves, and only succeeded in testing their I.Q's. The wolf bounty was eventually increased to forty dollars, but this age-old maneuver helped little.

The detachment at that time extended from Bowron Game Reserve to the Pacific Ranges, including a great stretch north and south. Few secondary roads existed, and those few impassable in winter, and budgets did not allow for aircraft or for little of anything else. Visiting all the nooks and crannies was delightful, but I wasn't too surprised to get the message, finally, that I wasn't supposed to visit them all. Our area was too large, but with ingenuity and a great deal of haywire we had improved upon destruction techniques neither perfect nor enjoyable: snares, traps, strychnine, potassium cyanide. No sooner had one pack been eliminated than another moved in. We had them surrounded, though one pack of ten infiltrated to within four miles of Quesnel.

Then Compound 1080 (ten-eighty)–Sodium Fluoracetate–reached British Columbia and created a "predator control" bureaucracy more difficult to eliminate than wolves. This insidious control operation became more widespread than is commonly known, for it was rarely discussed except at stockmen's meetings, and then in a hushed atmosphere. People rarely called it by its true name but instead referred to it as "certain methods" or "modern techniques."

Wolves stockpile kills at certain times during winter and, because they keep returning to these kills until all of it is eaten, they are easily poisoned. Their itinerary along these routes is quite reliable. Large packs of over six travel such great distances that they sometimes go into a ranching area for a time, and although the large packs seldom cause trouble, they do cause a great deal of fear. The very small groups near ranches are the ones that usually prey on domestic stock. Stockmen and others demanded more action every time they saw a wolf or coyote track.

The Predator Control Branch designed its 1080 program under top leadership, and for ranchers and sheep-herders.

Stringent measures were instituted with extremely restrictive rules, and domestic stock losses were quickly brought under control by air-dropping 1080-treated horse meat on frozen lakes. The program was a success in spite of the bad name 1080 had already received in the United States. No human deaths occurred, and other wildlife was not devastated unduly. But, paradoxically, when success was achieved, instead of being finished the program was stepped up. Total warfare. Even areas in which no domestic stock existed were to be blanketed with 1080 baits.

Compound 1080 is a deadly poison. I bought two old horses, two real old plugs, from Carl Nath of Lone Butte. Carl helped me butcher, but though I asked him to stay out of the way while I injected the meat he tried to help me. Having completed the rat-fink business I told him that he had to wash in the snow immediately, that he had to wash very carefully when he got home and before he kissed his wife. And I told him to make certain there was no blood on his clothing or boots and if there was to wash them. At the ranch, the dog started to lick Carl's rubbers and shortly afterward began acting so strangely that Carl let him outside. The body was found the next day two miles away. And just from a lick of stray blood.

Horse meat, or any other meat injected with the proper dosage of 1080, and air-dropped on frozen lakes to decimate wolves and coyotes is not particularly disastrous to other creatures. Not because other wildlife is immune to the poison, but because other species only rarely travel on frozen lakes, though the occasional fox, fisher, marten and wolverine does venture out onto them. But 1080 results in a slow death which allows poisoned animals to run for miles. Seldom is a dead animal or bird found, and for that reason little scientific data can be collected from 1080 victims. It's like sleuthing for the hole in the doughnut after the doughnut has been eaten. There is also a high risk of secondary poisoning to wildlife feeding on poisoned carcasses: jays and eagles and other birds regularly visit such baits.

Compound 1080 is, apparently, particularly toxic to the canine family, but baits sufficiently toxic to kill coyotes and wolves will also kill birds and carnivorous fur-bearers. Although an ounce of treated meat is more than sufficient to kill a coyote, he might eat several pounds. He leaves the bait, gets the staggers, regurgitates some meat; he recovers, continues on, staggers more extremely, and regurgitates some more; he runs, sits down and howls, hides, staggers on, and throws up everything he has eaten for the past week. By this time he is miles from the bait, but he has spread destruction as he went because this regurgitated meat is both highly toxic and highly attractive to other wildlife. You have then a chain-type poisoning among birds and fur-bearers alike.

Grizzlies, and other wildlife and endangered species, have been decimated on many alpine ranges simply for the "protection" of a small band of sheep. It is surely paradoxical that, as a result of pressure-group politics and a 1080-minded predator control branch, the wildlife department responsible for the grizzly's survival should also be responsible for the bear's disappearance from many ranges. Grizzlies wander from range to range, and baiting one alpine range with 1080 will exterminate them from several others. Sheep-herders are notoriously sloppy on our upland ranges: they seldom destroy sheep carcasses which then become food for bear and coyotes. And a bear or coyote caught feeding on such a carcass is accused of killing it, whereas the half-fed sheep dogs of badly-organized owners sometimes have to kill a sheep to survive, and may therefore be the real culprits.

I have visited many ranches in Central British Columbia and have noted that poor management brings with it high losses. But among thinking people the era of predator control carried to extremes is disappearing, because they are giving the widespread use of Compound 1080 a closer look. It will be a sad day, indeed, when we can no longer hear a wolf moan or see his hunting track, and we should be far enough advanced by now in our research to employ selective methods of control, if control is necessary. A return to older, more humane techniques would be an improvement, but they require a lot of knowledge to be used effectively. Far more than is needed to pry the top from a container of tasteless, odorless, colorless, undetectable death.

Nameless
Lake

*"It's the fresh air that does it . . .
wonderfully fine air it is, out here."*
Through the Looking-Glass
Lewis Carroll

Morning radiation fog shrouded the lake, all but the near shore, and filled the lower valley. Curling plumes raced out of fog banks, sped over the water and vanished: the cold air was moist and sun rays were already burning. A solitary loon called through the mists; an unhurried call, directionless, like the anguished reflex of a castaway, forlorn, forever searching a desolate land. I had awakened early only because I had had a good night's sleep, although a hundred-bird echelon of little sandhill cranes glided overhead. Turkeys, an Indian would call them. Their manner of flight and plaintive calls suggested they had flown all night: the sky had been clear and the moon nearly full. Perhaps the Liard Plain had provided their last food.

Sadsack performed his morning ablutions, then started on 121 my face as I pulled on my boots. I postponed my own wash—a ring of ice embellished the water bucket. We then walked toward fog-muffled bells. Two alien bodies had come to rest under the wagon during the night; one of them wore long hair and combs. The horses loomed belly-deep in billowing mist. Three were alert-eared strangers. I bridled the buckskin, removed his hobbles, and rode him to the lake for water. I fed him a handful of grain at camp, curried him down, and saddled up. Slim had coffee brewing and kokanee simmering by this time.

Our two guests were members of the Capoose family from the most southwesterly village of the Carrier nation—Ulkatcho, "place where all the animals are fat"—on an errand known best to themselves. It is not unusual for residents of this country to travel after dark, but travelling Indians usually avoid the camps of tourists because neither Indian nor tourist is comfortable. Slim and I, though, carry extra grub and welcome all to share our fresh eggs and our camp.

"I've heard there was an old trading-post near the west end of the lake," said Slim. "Know anything about it, Charlie?"

"Old building there one time. Might be nothing much left."

"We could paddle up and have a look."

"Hope you find something," I said. "See you after lunch."

Sadsack, Horse, and I took the trail west for a short distance then angled up the grassy slopes. I gave Horse his second wind on top. The fog had cleared and I glassed the scene below. Two coyotes mousing a flat to the west. Deer browsing nearby. A red-tail hawk soaring the ridges and slopes hunting for mice and ground-squirrels. An assembly of sparrow hawks on a snag, probably their nesting site, wheeling around one another in intricate maneuvers: this brightly colored grasshopper-and-mouse falcon would have been seen sitting on nearly any Russell fence in the Cariboo a few years back. Three bald eagles perched near their nest in a high old tree. There are thousands of them on the coast, but the interior population has declined tremendously. The bald eagle is a poor hunter and not a very good fisherman. Spawning suckers, kokanee, and trout provide some food. He picks up the sick and crippled, and beachcombs most of the rest. Or plunders better fishermen. An osprey fishing the lake was watched, I was sure, through eyes far keener than mine. He

122

had likely been supplying this family of eagles with part of
their food all summer. The eagle dives at the fish-laden osprey
until the osprey drops his load which the eagle sometimes
catches in mid-air, or when it lands on the water, though
sometimes the fish makes a getaway. Ospreys are good
fishers, and seem to accept this tax as unavoidable, although
they do screech about it. Continuation of the red tail hawk,
the sparrow hawk, the bald eagle and the osprey becomes
more doubtful each nesting season. Pesticide residues collected into their body fats while they are south are mostly
responsible for a yearly decline, but "varmint" hunters also
share the blame.

Our map showed a lake about two miles north, but indicated no name. We rode in that direction. Circling a pot-hole,
five moose crashed away through the timber and downfall. A
dry cow bellowed belligerently. Having no calf of her own,
she had apparently assumed responsibility for the herd.

In a glade of new pines and spruce and willows, snowshoe
rabbits had tracked small trails around a pool of spring water
and through the willows. One hopped away, appearing to be
very large because of his long hind legs and ears. The varying
hare is the true name of this species, because they change to a
white coat in winter. In winter their feet serve as snowshoes.
Rabbits are born naked and blind in a permanent-type nest;
hares are born with a snug grey suit in a hurry-up nest, eyes
open and alert. In summer, very early morning is the best
time to see snowshoe rabbits, but in winter they seem to be
most active at night. Small snares set on the rabbit trails
usually capture one by morning. We came onto old blazes,
and onto an Indian-style spring-pole trap of the size used for
snaring coyotes, fox, Canada Lynx and cougar dogs. Simple,
effective, outlawed, and inactive for several years.

As we started downhill the scent of the forest lay heavy in
the valley. Water sparkled through the pines, and spotted
sandpipers flew up to greet us. The real lake below matched
our objective on the map: a mile long; small meadow near the
outlet; another meadow ringing the north-west end; a stream
feeding in from the hills to the west. Picket posts driven into
the lower meadow; a water-logged raft on shore; weathered
fish-drying racks near an old campground: it had known
Indian fishermen.

Fish fed on the surface. Where trout cruised a gravelly bay

I tied up the buckskin and rigged my fly-pole. As usual, although having fished all my life, I had trouble threading line through the guides and tying on the fly. Having no waders I shinnied out on a partly submerged and shaky tree from where I could see a fish swimming by, forty feet out. I cast three feet in front of him. He took forever to reach the surface and to pluck in the fly. I set the hook–half-heartedly, for he was much too large for my leader–and he headed directly for a beaver-felled poplar. In trying to stop him I slipped off into three feet of water. I reeled in the parted leader, and Sack waded out to see what new game I had discovered.

Once over the initial shock, I thought I might as well wade the shallow bay and fish properly. The water wasn't unbearably cold, and the place was ideal for fishing. I could cast to a rising trout with no effort, or with equal ease catch a cruiser searching the water for insects. The trout were frisky and silver and fat, and weighed from two to five pounds. One very large one rolled near shore.

Indian summer filled the air and the sun was warm. Not numbed through, but cold, I built a fire, boiled a pot of tea and ate lunch. I grained the buckskin and cooked a trout for Sack. The usual hysterical loon examined us. Blue and green-winged teal, mallards, shovelers, ruddy ducks, goldeneye, bufflehead and scaups whistled around the lake. White-fronted geese sat on a point. Terns skimmed the surface and foraging muskrats swam the shore, busily restocking their cabins. Five fool hens sat in a row on a nearby log, cocking their heads and cooing softly. Canada jays floated in, picked over our leavings, and disappeared. Unusually quiet, intent on his winter larder, a red squirrel cropped cones from a tall spruce and let them bounce through the branches to the ground where he would later gather, peel, and skillfully arrange them into a perfect cone twelve to twenty-four inches high and leave them to dry in the sun, defying the clumsy-footed moose and deer to step on one. Dried mushrooms and other goodies he would already have stored underground.

A movement near the far shore attracted our attention. Five caribou, some of the stragglers who occasionally travel this region: a cow followed by a yearling, by a cow and calf and by a young bull. A peculiar, swinging gait, like a sophisticated woman on the run in a tight skirt. They were feeding on lichens along the game trail while on the move to a higher range for rutting.

I circled for the outlet creek which enters the Blackwater at Chinee Falls, intending to follow it to the general area of camp, but going was rough for the buckskin. I climbed him south-west into the timber where there was better going. I unsaddled him at camp and turned him loose. Slim and Charlie arrived soon afterward.

"Didn't find much," Slim reported. "Only the rotted logs of some old building. A few kickwilly holes, and some arrowheads. Three grizzlies were on the hill, west of the gulch you came down, and a char drowned himself." He hefted a ten-pounder from the canoe. "I've eaten enough fish. What'll we do with him?"

"Give him to the eagles."

We paddled to a rocky point near the eyrie, but to one which we could see from camp, and sliced the fish in two, and left it. Word of the party spread quickly. A crow scout arrived first, followed by his family of five; very quiet birds. Soon two ravens came, then one bald eagle. Canada jays and a black-headed jay kept coming and going with pieces of fish. Problems arose with two or three thieving mink. A rough-legged hawk circled over. The ospreys remained aloof.

Meanwhile, we had our second lunch.

"I hate to bring up the subject," said Slim, "but shouldn't we run downriver to-morrow?" We were looking forward to drifting down stream, but unfortunately that would be the beginning of the end of this trip. The natural community of lakes, streams, swamps, and hills was an uncluttered, peaceful place with room to stretch.

"Maybe we should pack the canoe to the second falls now; then we'll be set for morning."

"While we're there," Slim reminded me, "we could give those Dollys some fishing lessons."

We soon portaged over the game trail, through the woods, and around the "falls." Dolly Varden still lurked in the dark depths of the first pool where Slim rigged his fly-pole for light spin-fishing. He cast out, let the line sink down, and caught an eight-pound Dolly. It put up a good fight, but by boring deep and never breaking water. The next cast was better, but 125 he only caught a monstrous squawfish.

"Keep him!" I called. "Sack likes the bellies." So do I, if they come from cold waters.

This spot below the thundering chute was peaceful; the sun was setting and a cool westerly carried mist downriver. A kingfisher rattled his call while flying to his fishing perch and then, as Slim hooked another Dolly, the ragged-crested bird plunged into the river and flew off with a small fish clutched in his bill. Canada geese often spend the entire winter at the falls; and occasionally trumpeter swans and mallards feed in the fast water above them, as they do along other stretches of the upper Blackwater and remote coastal rivers. On a brilliant night, the deep-throated swan bugles in a silent, snow-filled valley, or sits like a cream-colored mound on shore-ice. On a rock in mid-stream, a water-ouzel bobbed from a crouch, like a spring-loaded sponge ball. The river-dwelling water-sprite, searcher of mossy, water-sprayed rocks, foaming pools and fast current, sent his golden warble across the ice-glazed boulders on even the coldest days. Beside some unfrozen rapid or bubbly stream, I've often hung up my snowshoes, boiled a pot of tea and listened to his song. Slim balanced on a rock, as close to the falls as possible, Sadsack perched on another rock watching. As though waiting for Slim to fall in. Charlie and I were unobserved, or so I thought.

Staccato chattering and scolding sounded from behind. Turning, I discovered two marten, one among the roots of a downfall, the other on a log. The one in the roots ran closer and for a moment I thought we were under attack. He stood up a dozen feet away, showed an orange-colored splash on his chest, and scolded again. When I gave him the mouse routine, he scrutinized me, and jumped onto the log. Like two small boys showing off before an audience the two friends rough-and-tumbled along its length. I squeaked again. They suspended their mischievous play, knew the squeaks were imitations, and resumed their chattering, rolling, tumbling game into the woods.

We started back to camp and were surprised by two mourning doves. They were quite a distance north of their usual breeding range and are the only two I have seen along 126 the Blackwater. "Sometimes see that kind at Nazko," said

Charlie. A bull moose with a forty-inch spread was across the lava bed a hundred yards below the lake, and seemed about to cross. We stalked to the thick screen of willows along the channel. He buried his nose in the swift water, as if testing it, and came across, chest-deep, hoofs more or less anchored to the bottom, hit the bank forty feet up-river, and heaved out with great gut-rumbling. Slim groaned like a love-sick cow moose with a bellyache. The bull whirled his head, rolled his eyes wildly, spotted us, and trotted off to the north. Slim groaned again.

"It's almost rutting season," I reminded Slim.

"Aw, there's lots of trees around," he said.

"Might be you better on a horse," said Charlie.

We built a tall-tale fire and enjoyed hot drinks. The otter swam by, turned momentarily to look at us, and continued on to the falls. Returning home or leaving? He had swum by last evening at almost precisely the same time. "Almost" because the daily living patterns change almost imperceptibly day to day; as the sun rises later and sets earlier on succeeding days, the animals adapt their habits to the hours of local daylight. The beaver, as Mackenzie noted, "allot for their labors . . . the whole of the interval between the setting and the rising sun."

"Heading back to-morrow, Charlie?"

"Yes, got to leave you fellows and get to work. Can make it easy in one day now."

Chapter Fourteen

Downriver

"The prettiest are always further!"
Through the Looking-Glass
Lewis Carroll

A brilliant sunrise danced across our rolling flat. Morning melt shimmered on the white-frosted shrubs and grasses. Stretching teal swished overhead, raised in a climbing turn, snapped their wings, sorted, and skidded into the bay.

"Some country, huh?" Slim ventured from the comfort of his sleeping-bag, rolling a smoke.

"It's cold." The horses whinnied at Charlie on the flat.

"How about ham and eggs and hotcakes for breakfast?" asked Slim.

"Sounds good." When Charlie came in with the horses, we harnessed the team and then sat down for breakfast. I asked Charlie if he had enough food to see him back.

"Plenty grub. Might be to-night I stop with Johnny. How long it take you fellows?"   129

"Two days. We could make it in one, but we'll be fishing." Into the wagon Slim and I loaded gear that wouldn't be needed, that Charlie would leave at the pickup or Johnny's. His departure committed us to river travel and the place seemed to become more lonesome. We packed to the canoe in one trip. On the way we saw a willow ptarmigan. The little white-tailed species has a pure white tail; both willow, the largest, and rock ptarmigan, of medium size, have black tails. White-tails spend most of their life in the crags and cirque basins above timberline, at Arctic alpine elevation where horned larks and pipits and pink snow-birds nest. These grouse, these ptarmigan, step differently from other grouse, and I have seen their tracks on summit ridges of plateau regions in the dead of winter.

Because the river was low and not too violent or swift, Slim maneuvered between the large boulders with little effort. But there were tricky places for the first mile, where we had to work along shore or line the canoe down or around small chutes or rapids. We took out once for a short distance. Two miles downstream we rounded a bend through rough but safe water, and one hundred yards ahead a rapid or small falls broke over immense rocks which were lying completely across the river and making the last rapid in the series of about five below Kluskoil Lake. A small gravelly flat lay to the north, and spruce and willow grew to the very edge, as along most of this distance. The brimming pool at the bottom of the rapid was just too inviting to pass up: I've never seen friskier trout. Up to three pounds and they came to nearly every cast. For lunch we enjoyed baked rainbow and Dolly Varden, and a drying out. We had been soaking wet by the time we stopped.

Gradually the rocks diminished in size and became lighter in color and less volcanic. Sack was on the north bank, but changed sides and was staying in sight. Perhaps a wolf was bugging him. At any rate, as the current slackened and the shores became swampy we took him aboard. Then about twelve miles below Kluskoil we passed the entrance to a small backwater lake which we didn't explore, but we could see in the timber on the north shore what appeared to be the remains of a log cabin. Perhaps one of Old Joe's hideouts.

Ducks traded up and down and we surprised flocks of

geese, several moose, and two black bear before we shot through the rapid at the outlet. The river maintained a generally southeasterly direction towards an unnamed mountain near Open Hole divide. Taking turn-about fishing from the bow as we glided through we cast behind rocks and into pools. Usually with immediate response. At the best pools we dropped anchor. Danger seldom comes to the birds and animals from the water, and for this reason man can approach them more easily, the geese and ducks, beaver and mink; even the careful cougar, wolf, and grizzly.

About four miles below this backwater lake we entered a widening of the river that flowed J-shaped for nearly three miles, and paddled seriously for the first time. Waterfowl were numerous: abundant eel grass and duck food. When we swept out of this water-fowl oasis into a smooth-flowing reach salmon darted from the center of the deep channel and when I stood up I could see several small schools of them downstream. Average seven pounds, with the familiar crimson spawning color of the sockeye. We passed perhaps fifty fish.

Unexpectedly we met a river flowing in from the south. Balustrades of spruce bound the shores, and deep waters curled to their roots. A fairly large island split the main river above the meeting-place, with a smaller one below. Park-like openings rose to the north, and open sidehills farther north still. Slim steered to a small sand beach, near the confluence which curved around an island delta, and a flock of geese arose. We wondered what canoeist had last stepped ashore. The fear-filled look of men seemed far away. Sack, who had been running along the bank, had swum the river, and gave one of his mournful howls of greeting. The Baezaeko was our camp for the night. Several hours of daylight remained: we'd have time to explore before dark.

A quick scouting revealed handy tangles of willow and poplar driftwood, peeled and chopped to campfire length by the beaver, and left stranded high and dry by spring flood. The grassy banks were spaced with birch, aspen, spruce and pine. Indian paint brush, yellow arnica, and white daisies were pressed into the hollows of high-water sand dunes. Tracks of coyote and fox showed in the sand, and those of mink, otter, and beaver along the stream. Deer, moose, and black bear signed on a well-travelled game trail. Red-naped sapsuckers, tapping on a birch, were indifferent to this intrusion of their domain. The scurry sounds of a ruffed grouse family came from the forest. Solitude and peace prevailed. Slim returned to the canoe for his fishing rod because trout were rising in a pool above the river.

"What fly are you going to try?" I asked after he had returned.

"A Cinnamon Sedge, I think. Hard to tell. Not much but the hook left. I should change. A new leader too. Any suggestions?"

This spiel was meant to do me out of flies and leader. I produced a box and we fingered through the grand assortment. Yet even when comparing the virtues of each we knew that almost any fly would interest these trout. We selected first a rather unconventional Stone-type hair-wing with a mottled-brown back and pale yellow-green body, plump and slightly flattened, nymph-style, and ribbed in gold with two long tails, on a number six. It would take fish almost anywhere. Another resembled a Teal and Green, on a number eight; and one was dressed somewhat like an Alexandra, on a number six hook.

Slim doesn't lose many flies to the trees and bushes. He uses a lot of Roll and Spey casts. He's unaware that he does so, however, and couldn't care less. A beginner first learns the basic overhead cast which is fine for lakes and open reaches, but of limited use along wooded streams and canyon pools. The easy-going Spey and Roll, applied to personal technique, develops a working easiness with trees and bushes. Otherwise a lot of good water is passed up. The short, stiff, American-style rods are hopeless for proper Roll and Spey casting; a supple rod, at least nine feet long, reaches just that much farther with comfort.

I picture large trout lurking suspended in the shade, securely hidden under overhanging bushes, plucking in the insects dropping to the water or drifting past, and my fly coasting through. I like to cast upstream if I can, to put English on the fly, or a shepherd's crook, so that the end of the cast shoots sideways under the bushes. Sometimes the fly doesn't go the way I want it to go, and lands in the shrubbery, but usually with a gentle tug it falls free like an insect. And

the fish is waiting! I ease him downstream, if I can, to avoid
alarming his sidekicks. The big, fat, red-meated ones travel in
pairs!

Slim picked a rise and the Stone settled like thistledown. A
three-pound rainbow flashed in the clear pool and snatched
it, and then burst out in a series of amazing leaps. Slim played
it firmly, yet patiently; appreciatively. He led it to a side pool
where I intended to release it, but because the stomach was
bulging I killed to examine the contents. It wasn't full at all:
one digesting salmon fingerling, possibly a chinook, and a
couple of bright green bugs. A fat trout and dinner for Sack.

Collecting the 6.5 and binoculars, Sack and I headed more
or less south while working up to a ridge. Soon the first bunch
of mule deer bounded off—three large bucks—then a pair of
fork-horns. I like to see two-year-olds together: a mother
must be healthy and life must be going well for the herd, or
else twins can never jointly survive for a year and a half.
Moose had been feeding on the tender shoots of upland
willow and red osier dogwood.

The really mature bull moose would still be higher in the
hills and not too easy to find, because they usually go into
semi-seclusion just before the rut. September 7 is the earliest I
have observed this temporary insanity in Blackwater.
Generally speaking, moose are not earnestly rutting until the
eighteenth or twentieth. Even game guides are at a loss some
seasons to know when the rut really began and ended, though
some claim that the first full moon in September sets the rut
into full swing. Some years it seems to be mostly over by
October 10, but it generally continues until the fifteenth.

Many signs indicate that moose are rutting: indifference to
man and indifference to food; pawing hollows in the ground,
often in spruce patches, in which they urinate and roll;
breaking brush and thrashing small trees with their horns;
calling by both sexes—especially morning and evening—the
cows a mournful, drawn-out summons, the bulls a shorter
groan that ends with a coughing grunt. Towards the end of
the rut the bulls call more plaintively, a sort of whistling
moan. And they fight, and though contests between bulls are
rarely fatal, they do produce serious injuries: gorings,
cracked and bruised ribs, horns broken completely off.

At a large meadow, one early October afternoon, I 133

climbed an Indian lookout tree in order to have a better view.
At the very far end, a mile distant, two bulls were fighting
and three or four cows looking on. The smaller bull put the
run on the big fellow which came up the meadow towards
me, moaning and talking to himself every two or three
minutes. He uttered a half-hearted grunt, and I answered
with my most traumatic cow call before he entered a small
island of spruce just out of range and remained there, silent
and completely screened while composing himself, for about
twenty minutes. Then, again muttering, he continued towards me. I climbed down from my tree and bellied through
the small willows to the edge of the meadow and stood up at
what I thought should be just the right moment, when he was
fifty feet distant. He saw me and ran, and even though I knew
the meat would probably be tough I tumbled him head over
heels with a shot through the neck. His stomach was completely empty, his rib cage badly bruised, and he was as gaunt
as a scarecrow.

Having gained the poplar-gilded ridges, I saw rolling
swales and a small meadow to the south, part of a string of
pot-holes or beaver ponds that drained to the Baezaeko. A
scan with binoculars showed an immense porcupine feeding
on slough grass; a pair of marsh hawks, the brown-colored
young of that year, flying a search; muskrats and ruddy
ducks on a gleam of water; a cow moose and calf picking
their way along the edge of a willow thicket. The crisp-sweet
smell of September. A brief mood of air and sunlight.

Several ruffed grouse flushed into a spruce. A few would
be nice for dinner. I shot the heads off three and Sack
retrieved them. Farther on, seven sharptails flew to a poplar
and I had two more. To go with them I easily found some
small but very strong wild onions, one of the first greens to
sprout in spring. This plant which the Indians call "coston,"
and which has a strong center stem and pinkish flower,
grows over most of the watershed, especially on open
sidehills, and somewhat resembles chive. Deer feast on the
tops in summer. We had brought spuds with us, but could
have had a type of wild starchy tuber that Old Joe calls
"Indian noodles." One place, near Dry Lake, he calls
"Noodle Meadows." The plant has a small, carrot-like top
134 and a little pale-blue flower. It grows about a foot high. The

tuber is a few inches underground. Another variety grows
like heavy yarn in an intertwining ball, often six inches in
diameter. Bear dig for them, especially in early summer.
Tracking a bear can lead to the different varieties as well as
to the small Indian potatoes found at higher elevations. Some
grow in meadows, some on hillsides, and others in the damp
ground under stands of spruce. Dry Lake and Poplar Mountain produce them in abundance. Wild parsnip, which must
not be confused with poison hemlock, grows in damp ground
along and near the streams and lakes; it is a very long-
stemmed and, at times, evil-smelling plant with pale-pink or
whitish flowers and parsnip-like roots. The green stems,
when peeled like coarse celery and boiled in two waters, are
not bad eating. The Indians also strip the bark from lodgepole pines in spring and scrape off the succulent cambium or
inner bark to eat. This practice accounts for the many
stripped trees along the trail. Indians also eat the small pine
seeds, as well as many other wild plants and berries. Especially Indian women like Minnie.

Indian women like Minnie had a use for everything and a
time for everything. Although the Carriers were mainly land
hunters, much of their food came from lakes and rivers—
fresh water fish, clams, beaver, muskrats, waterfowl, and the
salmon, steelhead and sturgeon which went up the rivers to
spawn. All were taken by nets, fishtraps or harpoons. Land
species were captured with spring-pole traps, snares and
deadfalls, in addition to the bow. Meat and fish, as well as
roots and berries, were dried for winter use. Fresh meat
snoozed in bear dens all winter until needed. Hides and furs
provided leather and clothing. If a man starved here, he was
half dead already.

Carpets of woven pine needles cushioned the trails for
silent strollers and left no sign of their passing. But Sadsack
sorted out a scent, raised his head and looked to me for
permission to leave the trail. A scratch-pile he found beneath
a gnarled pine was fresh enough that a few of his hackles
bristled. At least one cat had travelled through here on his
rounds. Perhaps cougars each carry a different odor: Sack
sniffed and snorted as if trying to memorize that one.

Chapter
Fifteen

Pussyfoot

*"And who is Dinah, if I might
venture to ask the question?"*

Alice's Adventures in Wonderland
Lewis Carroll

Much about cougars is concealed in their scratch piles, although little is decipherable by man. Cougars form these neatly-constructed sign posts by raking dry evergreen needles, or other debris, into compact little heaps four to six inches round and about four high, in which to conceal their urine and faeces. The operation is fidgety, time-comsuming, and thought-provoking. To build next an old one? Reconstruct a broken one? Build a new one? Where? The communal site or information center is usually under a large gnarled conifer overlooking or near a canyon or basin, and cougars carefully inspect it when passing on their mysterious business trips. If in a hurry, a cat will ignore less important places. Away from the communes practically any spot serves the purpose.

137

These "communes" give a good indication of the number of animals using the territory. Along the Quesnel River, for example, a country I have snowshoed through a good deal, I know of five main communes in the best one hundred square miles of cougar wintering range. I've counted twenty-four scratch piles around one tree: about ten adults checking in. Quite a community. Twenty years ago a house was built on top of a commune on a cougar route which went from one winter range to another, and eventually several houses appeared. The owners are probably unaware that cougars still travel this route through the remainder of woods.

Truly polygamous, with generally solitary lives and tempestous *affaires d'amour,* most of the cougar population by far is female. Kittens are difficult to sex, but I have examined a fair number of young cougars still with the mother, and found only a small percentage to be males, about three females to one male, certainly two to one. Females generally raise three kittens and frequently all are females. Makes one wonder how tom cougars come to be, although one can easily see why they lead such a hectic life.

Once a tom cougar leaves the protection of his mother, during his second year, he constantly risks being hunted down and maimed or killed, perhaps eaten by a larger tom. For the first year or two on his own he leads a solitary life, often finds another area in which to hunt, and remains as inconspicuous as possible until attaining some growth. Unless he is involved by some female on the search, he stays out of all intrigues until he is three or four years old.

These young toms may range widely because they have difficulty finding food, or perhaps some just wander to discover what's going on in the world and then find themselves in poor game country. Either way, an empty stomach doesn't entertain a happy disposition. Such a cougar may settle for a time, unseen, near a small village and pick off the housecats and dogs which seem simply to disappear from some "rare disease." Any dog that will bark can tree a cougar, but if a silent-running dog surprises the cat, the cat might make a stand and kill the dog.

At one place, three people with brooms and garden rakes swatted at a cougar which picked up the dog, a large heinz
138 and walked into the woods. Sadsack and I arrived at this

small community two days later, and on checking tracks I
found it was probably a tom. A logger told me that a farmer
nearby had a herd of goats running at large during the day,
and suggested that we pay him a visit. We learned that a goat
had failed to show the night before, and that the rest of the
herd refused to leave the farm. Sadsack didn't need any track;
he could smell the cougar and knew its exact whereabouts in
spite of the smelly goats and a couple of billys that he had to
teach to respect him. I had to call him back twice.

People think that a cougar is just a cougar. Not so: each is
an individual, especially an older animal, and I wanted to
learn all I could about this one before I let Sack go, because
I wasn't about to lose a good dog over the killing of a
mongrel. If the cougar was a confirmed dog-killer, as I
suspected, anything was fair: snare, trap, or rifle. But we
must not excite him in any way.

We returned to the original scene, from which I planned to
circle for three or four miles to find what there was to be
found. It wasn't the place I'd choose to hunt, but it was ideal
for snares. The trails were warrens. We were crawling
through a thicket when Sack committed the unforgiveable.
He sneaked off and left me, and headed for the goat farm in
full voice. I heard a shot. He stopped baying.

The goat-herder's daughter had also been listening. She
had cut through the bush to intercept Sack and, walking
along a trail, happened on the cougar with its back toward
her and lying on a downfall also waiting to intercept him. She
bored the cat through the shoulders with Pa's .416 Rigby.
When I arrived the smoke had cleared and I had nothing left
to do but nurse her bruises. Sack had been saved a severe
mauling. This large, slovenly, middle-aged tom was running
at the eyes—a rarity among cougars, he might have had
distemper. He had made one domestic goat kill, and I found
the remains of several dogs and housecats.

The possibility of anyone's being attacked by cougars is
remote, although they have attacked humans but killed only
once in my experience: a young boy. Most of the attacks have
been provoked by people who have been trying to save a pet
dog. Far more danger than comes from cougars really comes
from other, normally docile, animals that rampage for no
apparent reason, but the culprit which does attack is usually a

young tom, not a crippled or senile old animal as one might
suspect.

With Alan Gill, who has trailed many, I drove out one
winter's morning in his car. When climbing up a snow-bound
valley we crossed a cougar track on the road, and stopped to
look. It was only minutes old. Because we were distributing
1080 baits for coyotes, I had left Sadsack in town, but Alan
owned an old experienced cougar hound called Paddy. We
decided to take him out of retirement and hunt an easy
cougar. Other business can suddenly become irrelevant,
especially 1080. An excellent pistol shot, Alan was armed
with his .357. I had left my rifle in my car. Alan made me
take his .30: "You never know."

Back again we found that the cougar had re-crossed the
road. We slipped into our snowshoes and set out on the track
but the deep snow was too much for Paddy. We hadn't gone
far before he showed symptoms of having a heart attack.
While Alan comforted Paddy, I decided to follow the cat for
a way. This puss was particularly interesting: he had already
walked through the door of an abandoned cabin and out the
vacant window frame on the other side.

I hadn't gone more than two hundred yards when I came
to a rock slide and stopped. Everything seemed normal, and
plainly the track went on around the slide, but I had the
uneasy feeling that something was not quite right. I listened
for squirrels and birds, but heard none. The sun was well up
and the heavy snow which had fallen the night before slid
from the evergreen branches, which made a swishing sound
as they sprang back. I was jumpy, and I missed Sack. There
was little cover for thirty feet.

I followed the track a short ways farther to a small frozen
creek. A swish behind me. I turned. A cougar was thirty feet
away and was coming at me in long strides–fast!

Parky and fur mitts I had buckled on tightly. Cartridges in
the magazine of Alan's .30, but none in the chamber; a habit
of mine. Why I yelled "Alan!" I don't know, for he couldn't
help me; perhaps I had to let him know I went down fighting.
When I yelled, the cat crouched ten feet away–shoulder
bunched–an easy spring for him. My first reaction was to
reach for my knife, but mitts still on, I instead levered a
140 cartridge into the chamber and, aiming from the hip, pulled

the trigger with my thumb. The bullet caught him in the front
shoulder and shocked him badly for a few seconds as a poorly
placed first bullet usually does. Mitt off, another cartridge in,
and I put it between his eyes. An easy cougar after all.

When Alan arrived we followed the track I had been
trailing. The cougar had bedded down under a small spruce
two hundred feet farther on, had heard me coming, and
circled back. At the slide he had been standing behind a big
ponderosa, not six feet from me, had let me pass and go on
about fifty feet, and then had come after me. Alan said that
when I shouted I had sounded like a boy-soprano.

We suspected that something was wrong with the animal
and we performed a field autopsy. He must have had some
reason for being aggressive, but although we found an empty
stomach, we found no heavy infestations or old wounds, we
found normal eyes, and he was fat like a cougar ought to be.
Nothing unusual. We'll never know, of course, why he was
aggressive, but I do know that when I met his unwavering
stare and had seen his tail snap twice, that signal before the
leap, I should have pulled off a mitt, quickly slipped in a
cartridge, and stared him down. A bad year for that sort of
experience; I was beginning to suspect that I had an attractive
smell.

Alan estimated the tom at two years old; I said perhaps
three. We weighed him on Alan's beam scale at 105 with the
viscera out; not a large animal by any means, especially for a
mainlander. Vancouver Island cougars are smaller than
those on the mainland. I weighed one Interior male at slightly
under 200 pounds, and I've seen two others as large.

This one, though, obviously did not know how to go about
killing a man. He certainly had the opportunity to size me up,
but he did not make a normal attack. Killing a deer, for
example, he would have stalked to within forty feet, made
two leaps and, giving no warning, would have had the kill
over in seconds. He had moved in on me with long strides,
and not with leaps, and when I yelled, he had stopped, and
crouched. I had shattered his self-confidence.

Except for Mexico, British Columbia is the only place in
North America where cougars, or pumas, or mountain lions,
can still be found in numbers. This adaptable and curious cat
once ranged the Americas from the Yukon River headwaters

to Argentina's Patagonia, and Yukon Territory Indians tell
me that the cougar's range has gradually been extending
northward. No one has any real idea of the total cougar
population, but the species is most assuredly not endangered,
and we are only just beginning to understand the intricate but
natural predator-prey relationship that the cougar, as a
natural assassin, has with our deer herds. His role has finally
been recognized in British Columbia where, since 1958, he
has been classed as a game species. The bounty served no
purpose anyway other than to give a rather unreliable
record of the number of animals killed each year.

Cougars are the swiftest and most efficient of our large
carnivors. Their graceful movements and their singleness of
purpose permit them to get the enchanting business of shop-
ping and dining quickly out of the way, and leave a lot of time
for other enjoyment like intrigue and travel. They are also
playful. They love to climb trees, to stalk and leap on each
other, to catch a packrat and pester him for hours. One had
carried the bottom half of a Coleman lantern to his dog-and-
housecat slaughterhouse, and used it as a shiny toy.

Travelling light, Sadsack and I were camped once above
the head of a canyon about four miles north of the Quesnel
River. Quite a remote country and a long day's snowshoe
south of a main road. Trees and crags and crevices, and a
much-used "commune," suggested that it was good cougar
country. A handy grove of birch for firewood; a small
sweet spring which never seemed to freeze completely: no
need to melt snow and pick out spruce needles, tree lichens,
and rabbit leavings. A cougar-tracker should be tough.

This favorite bivouac under an immense spruce with a
wide canopy had obviously provided shelter for many cougars because, when first erecting our lean-to, I had scraped
aside a dozen scratch piles in the dry needles underneath. We
kept a small supply of emergency food here, cached in the
tree, and I had built some rough furniture. Essentially, we
had stolen the place from someone else, but it was kind of a
second home to us. Nevertheless, we didn't really expect
visitors to drop in. Besides cougars usually limit their travels
when temperatures reach 30° below, and make up for lost
time when temperatures rise. During an extended period of
142 cold weather I have followed tracks well over a week old, and

in a short distance found the cat comfortably holed-up with a kill or two.

This had been a long day, and we had been out two weeks. Our fire well banked with green birch, we settled into our sheltered place and left the wild night outside the circle of our fire. The wind hushing through the treetops sprayed finely sifted snow through the air, and roared with increasing speed beyond the rim of the canyon. My eiderdown didn't seem to hold any warmth, even with Sack snuggled down beside me with his head stuck through a poncho. It seemed terribly cold, about forty below. I replenished the fire at midnight and had just crawled back in when Sack let out a roar and nearly wrecked our cosy home as he exploded right through the wall.

I could hear him in hot pursuit and he soon bugled "treed" –in that wind he was barely audible a quarter-mile away. Putting on snowshoes and tramping through the darkness had as much appeal as a swim in the Quesnel River, especially when Sack seemed to have everything under control anyway. The cat would stay up there all night if necessary. But I then realized that with the cold and wind he might just come down to clobber Sack. I started out while Sadsack was still faithfully calling, and I looked for tracks with my flashlight before they drifted in. A female by their outline; she had followed around the hairpin-shaped rim and had been standing behind the spruce when Sack took her scent. No doubt she had seen the fire and had seen me in my orange long-handles.

I could see her near the very top of the large fir that Sack was saying she had climbed. Unusual. She was too far away for my small light and I didn't want to make a poor shot, but I set fire to a pitchy snag nearby and in the flare could then see her watching the proceedings, her tail hanging straight down. She was a gentle cat but the night was bitter-cold. I put one between her eyes quickly. My black-hearted pot-licker took his revenge on the carcass which I then skinned out and examined: a female of good size, several years old, one who had raised kittens at least once.

I have always regretted not back-tracking our visitor, at least back to her last kill, but because her stomach was empty I might have had to go quite a way. And tracking takes time, and who really cares what a night-prowling cougar did the last twenty-four hours of its life, especially when the temperature is forty below? She was plainly curious and nothing more, and had probably only wanted a little company and the warmth from our fire. Her prime pelt has been a soft bedside carpet for years.

An experienced adult cougar in good health, and hunting in a fair deer population, has no difficulty killing. Cougars do not leap from a tree as popularly believed, but stalk and then get onto the deer in two or three immense springs, landing high on the shoulders and neck. If they can't get onto a deer the second or third jump they will leave it and stalk another. With muscular shoulders, neck, and forelegs, they are tremendously powerful. The force of landing usually downs the prey, even a moose. Once on, the deer is theirs. The four prehensile canine teeth—two top, two bottom—are long and bevelled on the inside for tearing; the pointed molars overlap, the top ones on the outside for a non-skid, bone-crushing grip. Canines and retractible razor-sharp claws, including the two large dewclaws, come into action at the same moment. The cats often leave a hole in the back of the skull of a deer, as well as break his neck. They kill quickly, disembowel the animal, and eat the liver, lungs and heart first. They often bury the kill then by raking leaves, conifer needles, and deer hair over it. Some hunters claim that a buried kill indicates that the cougar intends to return to it quickly, but some don't return for weeks. Indians often salvage unconsumed portions.

An adult cougar kills an average of one deer a week, certainly not any more, but kills only to satisfy his immediate requirements, and an experienced cougar which makes a sickly or unsuitable kill might kill again immediately. Most of the population, like cougars with pressing business, young cougars, not-so-bright cougars, and females with kittens, take what they can get. All keep the deer herd alert.

A young, inexperienced cat will sometimes have difficulties finding food, but he will usually discover a sickly or crippled deer. If he does not, he might take to killing rabbits or porcupines. In fact, cougars seldom pass up the change of diet provided by a porcupine, but normally they get no quills in their mouths. On the other hand, I have yet to skin an adult mainland cougar that did not have quill particles under the skin of the forelegs. One young tom hunting culverts for porcupines had so many quills that he looked like a porky himself. He was a very inept killer, and therefore a possible menace to livestock. The occasional oddball will take a colt and, on what had once been a beautiful alpine meadow, one character killed fifteen sheep in one night, and ate not a morsel. I didn't get him: the sheep-herder kicked Sack.

I have examined many kills and have never seen a domestic cow, steer or calf kill that could definitely be blamed on cougars. They are too often accused of deeds for which they were not responsible; in fact many times the so-called prey was not killed by a predatory wild animal at all. I have examined several domestic goat kills where a cougar was guilty, but the goats were invariably on a poorly-managed farm where they ran at large like deer.

Many animals and birds benefit from the cougar kill, especially during the low of the ten-year cycle when rabbits and grouse become almost non-existent: coyote, fox, fisher, ermine, marten, wolverine, bobcat; jays, chickadees, ravens, eagles and some hawks. But seldom lynx; they are not eaters of carrion, and practically live or die with the rabbit and grouse population. Compound 1080 in cougar deer-kills devastates the wildlife community.

Cougars are fast, but I had never seen a cougar move any distance in high gear until the day Sack treed one in a picturesque fir. We had followed this tom for several days, learning cougar secrets, when he seemed to become petulant and not act normally. We let him cool off for a couple of days. It snowed heavily meanwhile, and I thought we might lose him, but we followed his dimpled tracks and finally met him head on, coming back on his track. He'd stood for enough foolishness. Sack put him up the tree.

I was taking pictures and further agitated him by nearly shooting off his branch and making him move to another. I tied up Sack, intending to take pictures and shoot the cougar simultaneously, but too intent on the camera, I pressed both releases. He slid down a few branches, hung on, righted himself on the bottom branch, leaped over Sack and streaked through the woods. Never have I seem an animal move so fast. On tracking him we found that he didn't give the impression of being hurt, but when Sack treed him again, I shot him properly. The first shot had creased his skull and knocked a chip from the cranial ridge.

Cougars are shy, and because they have superior hearing and eyesight people without a cougar dog seldom see them in the wilds. Many woodsmen have spent years in cougar country and seen none. Without hounds, I have seen only four. One of these at a cabin where there were penned beaver and also in summertime, when the deer and cougar were spread out on summer-range and could be seen almost anywhere.

At that time Ernie Holmes had launched an efficient beaver-trapping operation. He captured them in live traps and kept them in holding pens where, plied with delectables, they soon became tame. I was the shipper, and occasionally assisted him. We were trying to transplant pairs of these "active and sagacious animals," as Sir Alexander Mackenzie called them, to other areas where they would rebuild deplete populations, erect their "curious habitations" and, through their ingenuity, maintain a balanced wildlife community. Everyone loves a beaver, except farmers, ranchers, and road engineers. Sexing beavers is the difficult and messy job: we were seldom certain if mild-tempered Ethelbert was a boy-beaver or a girl-beaver. We made up for our ignorance, years ahead of our time, by dispatching no less than a quartette on any given mission, invoking blessings with crossed fingers, and leaving the intrigues to them. The best two gallant backwoodsmen can do. Although accustomed to spending a good deal of time in cold mountain streams, beavers do become cold while captive in the water-set basket traps, and for that reason Ernie checked his sets and collected the prisoners at daylight each morning. We had returned from our morning rounds and were having our second breakfast when Ernie raised his eyes from the table: "There's a cougar!"

Looking out I saw a large tom with an oversize head walking up the road from the boathouse and beaver pens. My rifle was in the pick-up which was parked outside and plainly in view. Ernie invariably has an arsenal in repair. But to find a rifle that would shoot, and for which he had the ammunition! He found both. Meanwhile, I didn't take my eyes from the cat, who was unhurriedly placing one pussy foot after the other. Shoulder muscles rippling, in full control, he continued
146 toward the cottage.

"Take him right through the window," I whispered des-
tructively.

"No. I'll sneak around from the back." A seasoned grizzly-tracker gone suddenly buck-feverish. He eased the back door open and I heard the lock squeak. So did the puss. A flash of reddish-brown: he was out of sight in the woods.

Male cougars travel many miles in search of a female, but females in season travel even greater distances to find a mate. Out tracking one time, we were four days before catching up to one female who had passed up dozens of deer, but had fed at an old kill and dispatched two porcupines for snacks. We had already snowshoed close to sixty miles, in one huge circle. The third day, or second night, she met two different suitors who had had a Mexican-standoff type set-to, and then laid up while she prowled with another boy-friend.

The females show great concern for their young. We once tracked a female and killed two spotted kittens of her family of three, but Sadsack couldn't decide which tree the mother and the other kitten had climbed, although we knew they were up a tree somewhere. Darkness came, we left the two dead kittens where we had killed them, and camped at a spring a mile away. She returned during the night to the two kittens and carried them away to where she had the survivor. We found them all the next day in a small cave.

When kittens are small the mother leaves them in her den while she makes the kill and feeds herself. When they are about five weeks old, at about a week before their spots start to disappear, she makes the kill and then returns for her kittens to take them to eat at the kill. She will have another den nearby, but from that time they really live a nomadic life. Always curious, with or without kittens, female cougars are always investigating old coyote and wolf and bear dens, and probably know of dozens in their territory.

Next to watching animals, tracking them, especially after a fresh fall of snow has settled, reveals most about their food, numbers, haunts, habits, and even moods. Tracks are not always fresh, and part of the game is to determine how old they are: the amount of frost in the track; whether made during a thaw or freeze; whether now frozen or starting to thaw; other animal tracks, over, under, across; and a knowledge of their habits. An adept tracker pokes, feels, and 147 examines; most important he remembers the weather for the past twenty-four hours, the times of winds, snowflurries, and temperature changes. When analyzing older tracks he recalls the weather for the past few days, and sometimes weeks. A good tracker, who can identify any animal track at a glance, is subconsciously a portable weather-recorder.

Two other members of the cat family also inhabit the Blackwater basin. Quesnel has been about the northern limit for bobcats, an animal about four times the size of an average family cat but, in recent years, they have extended their range thirty miles north from Baker Creek to the Blackwater River. The Canada Lynx is another; about bobcat size, and with built-in snowshoes for feet. He lives throughout Central British Columbia and the North. Bobcats "tree" readily, but lynx often leap from tree to tree like a fisher. Lynx, though, do most of their rabbit hunting through a burn or a second-growth forest. Their tracks are often mistaken for cougar, but lynx walk practically on the surface of the snow no matter how loose or deep it is, while cougar sink nearly as deep as a man without snowshoes. A cougar track too is much larger but almost identical to that of the common housecat. Lynx are very pretty and inoffensive cats that stand long-legged and shadow-like, ear-tufted, watching from the side of a trail. Very occasionally lynx take domestic fowl, and even lambs when hard pressed for food during the low of the ten-year cycle.

Occasionally cougars have to take moose or caribou, but the cougar population depends almost entirely on the deer population. Generally speaking, no deer, no cougar. From December to April the deer congregate on their wintering grounds, on the slopes of the larger valleys, mostly below 3,500 feet, and because cougars are largely dependent upon deer for food, they too confine their travels to these ranges or pass from one to another, keeping on the fringe, just above the deer concentrations.

After trigger-happy deer hunters have gone home; after these greatest hazards to man and dog have been eliminated, winter is the easiest time to hunt cougars: one sees more tracks, and can choose a trophy-size animal with a prime pelt, and also the hunter has the woods to himself. Travelling 148 to the area during this season can be a problem, with back trails impassable, and jeep roads in such bad shape that one must snowshoe, but snowmobiles have simplified matters considerably.

These ranges are in semi-mountainous, fairly steep terrain, demanding good snowshoe equipment for constantly climbing a hill or sliding down one. I weigh about 170 pounds, and find 11 by 48-inch Ojibwa frames the most suitable all-around size. Minnie re-strings them; her work is strong and cleanly finished. I'm rough on these light frames and usually break one or two each winter. I carry repair material, bamboo splints and babiche, in order not to be caught miles from anywhere with broken snowshoes; a length of latigo also comes in handy for many jobs besides repairing broken rigging. Well-fitting harness is essential, because rigging that binds or rubs in cold weather quickly frosts a toe.

Clothing is important too, for it must allow perspiration to disperse freely. I wear leather-top rubbers, but after ten below switch to eiderdown socks and native mukluks which are light, and also make good camp slippers. Woolens should all fit loosely: socks, shirt, Cowichan sweater, and light, wolverine-trimmed parky. A woolen stocking-cap, with slits for the eyes only, in case of a head-on wind. I usually snowshoe in my shirt or underwear and pull on the extras when I stop to boil tea. Goosedown underwear is also fine for sitting around camp, and makes good pyjamas when temperatures are low.

Snowshoeing is a pleasant sport in itself. One soon feels the rhythm, and learns to use the built-in spring of a good pair of snowshoes, and one wonders if it isn't easier than walking. These trips through the winter-ranges are the ones I recall with nostalgia.

Baezaeko Bunnies

Where do you come from. . . .
And where are you going?"
Through the Looking-Glass
Lewis Carroll

Slim was fishing a pool farther down the Blackwater when Sadsack and I returned to our Baezaeko camp. The grouse were plucked–not skinned–and in a marinade, when he arrived at sundown.

"Got some chickens, huh? Aren't you afraid the game warden might catch you?"

"The season opened this morning."

We fashioned Baezaeko cocktails and settled back to compare notes. Slim had lost track of the number of fish he had released, but had seen four otters. Mother otter had stood on a beaver house and barked like a small dog to tell Slim that he wasn't welcome to use her river. A few sockeye were spawning. He had caught several three-to-four-pound trout in the Baezaeko, and a gob of worms had taken a ten-pound Dolly 151

Varden. The hook had lodged in its gullet and the fish had bled profusely. Slim killed it and left it on the bank while he explored upstream but when he returned three mink were tearing the fish apart. He cut it up, and in the end they were taking pieces from his hand.

I have taken large Dolly Varden from much smaller streams, but it does not always follow that large fish will be found in them. Present at a certain time one year they may not be the next. Much depends upon yearly conditions, on temperature and flow, on food, on fishing pressure, and on the fish themselves. They ascend some streams during high water in spring or early summer and have been resident for some months when fall spawning time arrives.

The Baezaeko is well populated with them. In fact, almost all waters which eventually go to the Pacific support at least some large ones. Many people slight the Dolly Varden, treat them as a coarse fish, and forget that in other parts of the world people consider them a top sport fish and very good to eat. Spending a day getting to a Dolly hole and then fishing it is one of my own favorite pastimes. In small tributaries, these places are usually in some nearly inaccessible canyon, some even within sight of a main highway.

As fishing pressure increases, and stocking of more desirable species continues in these waters, the Dolly could have difficulty surviving, except that the mature fish are often difficult to catch. Some migrate like steelhead to the comparative safety of the ocean for a time and later re-enter the system to spawn. Sea-run Dollys hit the rivers in silvery condition, their salmon-colored spots with a light-blue halo just faintly discernible. Sumptuous table fish when stuffed and baked! Better perhaps than when taken from their real home, the clear, cold, spring-fed mountain streams, or tarns at five or six thousand feet.

Both the Baezaeko River and its tributary the Coglistiko River head to the north of the Archies, on the slopes of 5,860-foot Baldface Mountain adjoining the Chilcotin River headwaters, in a remote and seldom travelled country. A pick-up can go to the junction of the two drainages; from there to Kluskus by wagon. This road leaves Nazko from Paul's trading post and runs near Fishpot Lake for a short distance

on the top of eskers, on those narrow sinuous ridges de- Baezaeko
posited by glacial streams cutting through and under the Bunnies
wasting ice cap and sometimes resembling railroad grades. A
fire-suppression jeep road, recently pushed through into the
upper Baezaeko country, follows the old Indian trail for about
twenty-five miles, from near Fishpot Lake toward Baezaeko
Flats, the headwaters of the Baezaeko. This road ends at
about the lower range of caribou.

The Baezaeko is a good trout and Dolly Varden stream. I
have ridden along much of it and near Coglistiko Lake I
found it slow and winding. The river flows in the bottom of a
deep trench most of the way to the Blackwater and drops
quickly through narrow stretches. There are some meadow
flats and benches, and many picturesque camping places.
There are no falls below the lake but there are quite a number
of rapids and many sweepers. The numerous and steadily
working beaver along both the Coglistiko and Baezaeko have
a deplorable aim and fall poplar trees across the rivers. A
goose-hunter descended the Baezaeko in a car-top boat and
ran into sweepers across the river: he lost boat, shotgun, and
nearly his life. I would only try it in a rubber boat, because
the rubber boat is more easily handled in this type of river.
The upper Coglistiko drains a high, meadow-muskeg country, and winds through a deep, meadow-bottomed trench for
most of the way to Coglistiko Lake.

Sadsack had hollowed a bed in the dry needles under a
spruce, to his evident satisfaction, and one baleful eye followed the proceedings. He suddenly sprang to life, voiced his
watchdog woof, and in moments we heard the sound of
horses and the creak of saddles.

Two Nazko Indian girls astride wild-eyed pintos came into
view. They wore fringed and beaded buckskin jackets, blue
jeans, dark cowboy hats and bright neckerchiefs. Rifles pro-
jected from saddle skirts. Ropes buckled on, small packs tied
behind the cantles. Rigged double-cinch. A pair of riders
equipped to look after themselves and capable of travelling
wherever their whims sent them.

"Tahootcha, Bill, Slim," said the older girl shyly. "What
you doing at this place?" ("Tahootcha," which really means
"What's new with you?" is also a greeting.)

The girls had been riding hard and were soaking wet, but meant this surprise visit to be a great lark. Suppressed giggles threatened to overflow.

"Just mosey-poking around, fishing, and one thing and another," I said. "Aren't you girls a long way from home?"

The giggle-bubble burst as if I'd just told the funniest story ever. "No-o," she said. "We been hunting Joe's mootase. Heard you shooting, so drifted over for a look-see." While hunting Joe's stray cattle through broken country to the north, they had crossed the Blackwater a half-mile or so downstream. One horse was a duck in the fast rocky river, but the other rolled and kicked up a dangerous fuss.

"It's hard to keep secrets around Nazko. You look wet, and that river is getting too cold for swimming."

I was surprised when they dismounted for Indian girls alone in the woods are skittish as doe deer. The girls dried out around the fire and I poured coffee while Slim unsaddled their horses. This bivouac was taking on character: a skunky dog, toasting Indian girls, grilling grouse, boiling coffee, and the horsey odor of drying saddle blankets. A heady atmosphere. The saddle guns were pulled out of their scabbards for a cleaning. We turned the canoe over and I set the table for four people: "Cook'll have supper ready in a few minutes," said Slim.

"Your gun's not heavy," said the older girl, critically examining my rifle. "Make pretty slick saddle gun."

"Too 'spensive for us," said the other.

Wearing his gaunt look and sucking his cheeks in, Sadsack obviously thought he was suffering until the girls petted him, and he then gave me some nasty glances. His tattered ears stroked, he was suspended in seventh heaven. His trout had disappeared, but Slim soon caught him two more which I wrapped in foil and buried in the sand under the fire, and over which I then raked coals. When they were cooked Sack made short work of these as well, and then went back to his new friends.

I dished up a chuckwagon dinner: grouse, onion sauce, biscuits, beans, baked potato, salad, tomatoes, peaches and fruit cake. Everyone ate ravenously and counted me as a pretty good cook. I couldn't have missed.

154   The girls later sand-washed the dishes while talking softly

in their intricate Carrier language, the language of the Blackwater basin. As might be expected, Chilcotin influences spill
in from the south and Bella Coola influences from the west,
but the sing-song Carrier is beautiful to the ear when spoken
properly. It is heavy on clenched teeth and roof-sticking
vowels, and to use it a non-Indian must almost learn to speak
all over again. Some people say that you need ten years to
learn the language, but I've been trying for twenty, and about
the only term I use correctly is the one for bothersome Indian
dogs–"heist," followed by a clicking "tu-tu-tu"–go home,
get lost.

The creamy duskiness of the girls' smooth-textured com-
plexions reminded me of some Central European women.
The dainty features, delicate bone structure, and erect car-
riage, of some Asians, but with lighter-colored hair and eyes.
Almond-shaped eyes, definitely Oriental; the high cheek
bones of the northern provinces. Slender, tapered fingers.
Voices pleasantly modulated, the way a woman's voice
should be.

"Did you meet Little Charlie Cremo?" I asked. "He left
Chinee Falls this morning." No, but they had seen his tracks.
Nothing I could say would be news. What they hadn't themselves observed had been filled in for them by the moccasin
telegraph, at times an inexplicable combination of word-of-
mouth and telepathy.

"We have a tent you can use," I offered. "If you haven't
other plans." No, they said; they would continue up the
Baezaeko and hunt cows there to-morrow.

"Have you enough food?" The glances they exchanged
told me that they didn't have too much.

"Would you like a couple of trout for breakfast?"

"That would be nice," said the spokesman. "We've been
wondering if we should go in to Nazko for grub."

We helped our visitors saddle up, and gave them food
enough to keep them going another day. They had rifles and
probably fishing gear; blueberries and grouse were plentiful.
Undoubtedly they knew plenty about finding food.

"Don't have to worry about those two," said Slim, after
they had gone. "Raised on ponies. Eyes like a cat's, and know
every inch of the country."

It was quite dark by now, but a hunter's moon was rising. I 155 thought I'd seen a large fish boil several times below a rock in the pool in front of our camp. I examined the fly I had on and wondered whether I should use a lighter-colored one. Sorting through the fly box I found a full-bodied white moth on a splendid No. 6. The spent wings and heavy body were not dead white, but opalescent. It had been in the box for years, and I could only guess where I had acquired it.

It looked suspiciously like a Doctor Baker creation. Doc said he tied his own flies to keep his fingers supple, but because he seldom needed a fly-tying vise I suspect that he tied flies during the winter evenings mainly so he could daydream about trout fishing. This moth I had now was not what I called a Doc Baker Special: his almost coal-black fly in several variations of fur and feathers, usually on a No. 10 hook. I recall using it long after dark, anchoring over a shoal and not having enough will power to pick up and go home, but dispelling any fixed theories about light-colored flies being best for fishing in the dark of late evening.

I attached a new leader, and put up the opalescent when the fish or his brother rolled again. I waded out and sized up the lay: a fair cast. Eighty feet of line free, the fly dropped behind the boulder. A swirl. He was hooked solid. Nothing happened for a couple of breaths. Bull-dogging, down deep.

The eruption, when it came, seemed to carry him ten feet into the moonlight. He ran into darkness downriver and my backing splice shot through. More by feel than anything else, I worked him gradually back into the pool, his runs and leaps becoming less and less frequent. Slim handed me the net. The round, deep build of the prime rainbow–about six pounds. He might have been a small steelhead.

We unrolled our beds on the beach. Sadsack retired to his hollow to take up his duties for the night. My thoughts returned to sockeye and why there were so few of them on this fine stretch of spawning ground. Perhaps some catastrophe had befallen this run, or perhaps it was only just arriving.

Sockeye have rich red meat and are the most prized by the canneries. They spawn in rivers having headwater lakes, or on-course lakes, and spend their first two years–occasionally one and sometimes three–living with their fresh-water cousins, the kokanee. The smolts then migrate to the sea and grow quickly on the shrimp and small crustaceans that live in the fertile Subarctic Current of the North Pacific. When four or five years old, weighing five to fifteen pounds and averaging seven, they return to their birthplace to carry on the species.

A wonder, these salmon, and the journey they take from their wanderings in the broad Pacific, into the hazardous Strait of Georgia, homing first the arterial and turbulent Fraser and then the Blackwater. Their single-minded purpose and their tenacity seem to be greater than in any of the other living creatures. A precarious beginning and a sorrowful end: only the sea gave them freedom, only the strongest survived, only the fittest propagate.

Indians have told me that by mid-July the Chinook salmon are starting to appear in Blackwater tributaries. This run must be an early one, for chinooks use the spawning beds below the Nazko River in early August. The Baezaeko Indians take a few chinooks and a few winter-run steelhead. Salmon and steelhead ascend the Coglistiko to the falls which are many miles past Coglistiko Lake. Stomachs from Dolly Vardens taken near the Baezaeko-Coglistiko confluence contained salmon fry, and both Chinook and sockeye ascend the Nazko at least as far as Clisbako River.

Sockeye in the Euchiniko system go as far upstream as the outlet of Klunchatistli Lake. I have even seen a few in the Euchiniko above and below Hanham Lake, a few between Boat and Titetown Lakes, and a few in the lower reaches. The lakes of the Euchiniko system, at least Batnuni, should be ideal for rearing sockeye.

Unfortunately, only rudimentary data has been compiled on Blackwater salmon runs, partly because of the greater importance of larger river systems like the Quesnel and Chilco, and partly because of a lack of access roads. The Indians report salmon spawning in the creeks near Kluskus. Jerryboy, who possible knew more about the salmon, steelhead, lake char and Dolly Varden than anyone, noted "plenty" of sockeye below Kusyuko Falls, and he had caught steelhead in Euchiniko Lakes in winter. And Bunch Trudeau reports "fair numbers" of sockeye along the river channels joining Euchiniko Lakes. The Fisheries preliminary records vaguely show that a few hundred chinooks and a few sockeye travel to the Nazko to spawn, and these estimates were taken from fixed-wing aircraft over a spawning ground below the confluence of the Nazko and Blackwater. Apparently no one counts or records the salmon anywhere above that point, but Fisheries does agree that "the river has some nice spawning and rearing areas and has potential for more production."

Its full potential, then, has still to be officially determined, and it is a long time since Alexander Mackenzie was near Lesehetcha, watching salmon going up the Fraser, "driving up the current in such large shoals, that the water seemed, as it were, to be covered with the fins of them." According to Johnny Slash, for a number of years before the pattern of all Fraser River salmon was destroyed by the Hell's Gate blockage in 1911, salmon "filled" the river. He also says that, after having travelled so far, salmon taken from the Blackwater are not fit to eat, and that people should eat other kinds of fish of which there are plenty around for the catching. For salmon, he said, the Indians have always gone to the Fraser.

But he also said that the Fraser salmon are smaller, darker, and more slimy than in the past. No doubt the large fires of past years were damaging to them. As yet, logging has had little effect on the fishery, but if pulp trees in the upper basin are harvested in the usual manner, it will rapidly deteriorate, and from the mouth of the Blackwater I can already smell the Prince George pulp mills, fifty miles north. Their crud-foam cakes the back eddies.

Chapter
Seventeen
Supper
at the Bridge

"Soo — oop of the e — e — evening,
Beautiful, beautiful Soup!"
Alice's Adventures in Wonderland
Lewis Carroll

A pale radiance grew stronger behind the mountain outlines, Venus sparkled then flickered out, the sudden burst of a slice of sun streamed over the hills, reached our chilly valley, and spread light to the river that had spilled from a thousand crannies and nooks. Our Baezaeko campsite had proved to be a popular goose retreat, a late-evening meeting place. Moonlit silhouettes with heads canted had honked up and down the river half the night. Some flocks had all but sat down, and then scrambled madly when they discovered that their bar was enemy-occupied.

Slim was asleep. I could claim first crack at the pool above camp. I dressed quickly, quietly pocketed some figs and hardtack. Sack was ready and we sneaked off together. Wood ducks sprang from the pool and swept up the Baezaeko.   159

The two big strangers side-by-side near the tail-end of the pool must be steelhead. The pool was small and fish this size couldn't be expected to stay in it. I changed to a heavy leader, and then put up a sort of Polar Shrimp on a No. 4, gold-plated, short-shank hook; all fingers as usual. I cast short, across and up. One fish made for it, but I struck too early. The next cast was wide, but the smaller one came and I was in solid. He leapt, for what looked like six feet, and headed downriver. I peeled off jacket and vest and let him go, went into the river immediately and followed him down, half-floating on tip-toes around brush and logs, giving plenty of line.

Slim was starting the fire as I crawled to shore.

"Man are you wet!" he said.

"Cold, too. Take him a minute."

"You've got a good one."

"Not yet, but he's nearly done."

I worked the fish in and Slim captured her, a doe of about eight pounds, and sporting a bright rainbow stripe along the lateral line and gill covers. Slim held her for a moment, then let her scoot away. I told him that there was a bigger one up there, but that it had to have time to get over the scare I had given it.

"Okay. Let's eat first."

We returned to the pool, but the other wouldn't take. Still, there was no shortage of trout and the morning slipped by, and before we knew it, it was lunch time. We then loaded the canoe. Well into the afternoon we pushed off, looking forward to about eight miles of easy river and lots of fishing on the way to the upper bridge, where we hoped the pick-up would be parked.

For canoeists from Basalt Lake, the most westerly lake in the system, to the Euchiniko River, the Blackwater is a pleasant jaunt for almost anyone. From the Euchiniko to the lower bridge the Blackwater is wild and dangerous. From the lower bridge to the Fraser, I want no part of the Blackwater at all, in spite of Mackenzie's accepting the Indian account that it is navigable for their canoes. In fact, even from the Euchiniko Toa-thal-kas changes character, and it changes to one I do not like.

160 The pleasant and easy jaunt begins at Basalt Lake which

lies in timbered plateau country at 3,600 feet. Fingers of Supper meadowland extend through the timber in all directions, and At the cover roughly a quarter of the nearby plateau. A small outlet Bridge flows to Eliguk Lake, one mile east. The channel, which is deep enough for canoes, meanders through open meadow-land all the way to Eliguk, but obstructions necessitate canoes being pushed or lifted at a couple of places. Eliguk is four miles long and one of the best trout lakes in the water-shed. Near the Grease Trail along here I have seen salmon-sized trout on smoke racks. The outlet stream of the lake is called Ulgako Creek, and it joins the Blackwater about three miles below. A horse bridge crosses Ulgako Creek half-a-mile below Eliguk and the Grease Trail skirts the north side of the drainage.

Below the confluence of the Ulgako and Blackwater, the meander continues through meadows and open-type country most of the way to Tsacha Lake, or at least to the waterfall about three miles above Tsacha. Tsacha has several forested islands, favorite nesting places for Canada geese. Moose and deer also sometimes retreat to them to have their young. Prevailing winds are from the west: with a light breeze, leeboards and a small sail save a lot of paddling on these bigger lakes. A rapid lies immediately below the outlet of the lake but the short portage is a good one. Downstream to Kusyuko Falls the river is rough and requires some lining, but it is still navigable. Giving little warning, Kusyuko Falls thunders straight over a lava bed in an even cascade of about eighteen feet, and is the highest falls on the main river. There is some fast water too in the mile from Kusyuko to Euchiniko Lakes, but from there to Chinee Falls just fast water, rocks, and sweepers, along with the other normal hazards. I would allow about six days to make the trip.

In our aluminum canoe Slim and I had gone down from Chinee Falls to our Baezaeko camp in an easy-fishing eight hours. And the drift was to be just as easy from the Baezaeko camp to the upper bridge where the Nazko flows into the Blackwater. From the upper bridge downstream to the Euchiniko River is another painless day, with only a few no-account rapids and the odd sweeper. Nevertheless the chan-nels, bars and rapids are constantly adjusting, and she's wild when high.

BLACKWATER RIVER The Indian tribes of the Interior Plateau traditionally fashioned their canoes from spruce bark which was bound to a hardwood frame with watape—the long tough rootlets of the spruce tree, split into pliant, slender strings. Pitch sealed the joints and weak spots. The tribes also built dugouts, but construction was simplest with spruce. In early summer, to peel the bole of a thirty- or forty-inch Western white spruce is not difficult, and a suitable tree would have scarcely a branch for thirty feet. A twelve-foot spruce canoe hanging in a tree near the Chilako River had the bark turned inside-out over the framework, and was a real work of art.

From the Euchiniko to the Fraser the distance is twenty-seven air miles but, as a beaver drifts, the distance is nearer fifty. The lower Blackwater bridge is just over half way. The lower half is wilder and certainly more dangerous than the upper half, and jettisons the drainage of 4,630 square miles of lakes and swamps and muskegs into the Fraser.

Many of the canyons are easier to enter than to escape. Hundreds of feet below the plateau rim, slashing deeply through the Telegraph Mountain Range, the Blackwater twists and heaves its way through cuts, rapids, and convulsive switchbacks to the Fraser. Like a dark and furious serpent, the fast, constricted water hisses and thrashes past rock outcroppings, lava flows, slick canyon walls, and past slides of silt and gravel. Spring flood piles monstrous log jams and sweepers in the scarps and rocks, and leaves them above and below when the river falls. Low water leaves some leisurely water, some excellent fishing, and some pockets of gravel to be washed for gold.

From the Euchiniko it is a rough and dangerous run, but it can be navigated. If I were launching at the bridge near Gillie's Corner, I'd at first paddle lightly down the slow-moving Euchiniko, and brace myself for Boulder Rapid—rough at any water level, and a mild sample of what lies ahead. Check the dangers of each run from the cliffs or banks. About four miles below Boulder Rapid is Slide Rapid, merely fast at high water but rocky and dangerous at low. Nearly half way between Euchiniko River and the lower bridge is Rudin Canyon: a fast stretch about three miles long; 162 rocky when low water, long curlbacks and big waves when

high. Immediately then into Limping Wolf, one of the longest
and roughest at any water level; and about two miles below
and just past a small creek, Knauf: both these rapids have
large boulders, fast water and rough curlbacks. Next we can
see Slash Gulch a hundred yards ahead, but are already
nearly into New Rapid, which was formed by an ice blockage: swift water, and sharp rocks which might eventually
flush into the canyon and create real problems there. Slash
Gulch: a high-walled gorge, 500 feet long and thirty feet wide
at the entrance, but at low water only four feet wide halfway
through, and frequently tree-jammed. About 150 feet into
the canyon, most of the river sweeps against the north wall,
chews into the rock and disappears. Harder rock then forces
the water back into the channel lower down, where there is a
curlback of exceptional speed. The canyon widens as the
water finally plunges out. The cliffs are still precipitous for
another two hundred feet, but once out of this turbulence
the river is more peaceful. The canoe, however, would most
likely resemble an old beer can.

From the lower bridge to the Fraser is almost one contin-
uous rapid. An upset here leaves little hope. I ignore this final
section ever since I smashed the bow of a fourteen-footer in a
nasty little canyon, complete with switchback, two or three
miles down. The last-known Indian to travel down the lower
Blackwater in his spruce bark canoe was Tonass Jonquin,
who did it around the turn of the century. He arrived at the
Fraser intact, with an unknown payload, and paddled upriver
to an Indian encampment at Stone Creek. Years after Doctor
Baker had shot the lower river with Joe and Phil Lavoie, he
said that any man who would try it in a canoe must be crazy.
The road is less exciting but more certain.

From Gillie's Corner to the lower bridge it more or less
follows the Grease Trail, which is one to three miles north of
the river. Below the bridge, and on the north side one to four
miles back from the river, a logging road leads to the site of
Lesehetcha, the ancient village two miles above the Blackwater, which I suspect is about the place where Mackenzie
cached his canoe and buried supplies before setting out for
the Pacific, and which means "where the hillside moves and
slides."

Slim and Sack and I were far down the Blackwater by
evening. The trout were not quite so abundant below the
Baezaeko: in the best pools they only came to every other
cast, but averaged about the same weight, three pounds per
big one.

Crimson cirrus sutured the high sky which had been
sponged clean by altocumulus cloudlets. Twilight groped its
way up the gullies from the dark blobs gathered in the spruce
bottoms, and crept through pine terraces where yellow-
leaved aspens and white-skinned birches caught fire from the
dying day. We slipped down a dark velvet drape with gleam-
ing boulders spilling silver at the folds. Then, around a
sweeping curve and into the red sky, the river turned abruptly
southwesterly from its easterly course. Our free ways were
nearly ended.

"When we swing east again, the bridge should be about
one mile farther down," I announced to Slim. "About twenty
minutes."

Sadsack was chest-deep in the river, facing a group of
bawling range cows with calves.

"Sack's in wrong," said Slim. "Let's take him aboard. We
let every cow and wolf put the run on him. He's earned a
ride." Sadsack crawled to a rock, shook himself, and stepped
into the canoe.

The bridge loomed up ahead of us, we passed beneath it,
and we beached below. A campfire glowed and the pick-up
was parked nearby.

"Hello this place!" I called to avoid being mistaken for a
teepee-creeper.

"Hello, Bill; Slim; Sacky," called Minnie Trout Lake. "I
think you be along now!"

"Tahootcha, Minnie. All alone here?"

"All alone!" she giggled.

"You have supper yet? We're hungrier than a couple of
bears!"

"Yabut I fix dinner. You fellows like moose steak?"

"Sure, but you don't have to cook it."

"I never mind. I think maybe you don't like me to stew
smoked fishroes, but lil' clams from the river been cooking
long time. I got eulachon oil, fresh, too."

164   The river clams average four inches long, and Minnie had

chosen the tenderest. Mackenzie had found that the boiled Supper
roes would have been "not unpalatable" had they been "un- *At the*
adulterated by the stinking oil," but I did wonder, though, *Bridge*
where she would find eulachon oil in September, and fresh
eulachon oil at that. But knowing better than to argue with a
good cook, I merely said okay, and that she could choose
from the grub box anything she thought would fit her menu.
Slim and Sadsack watched impatiently, both famished, but
Minnie had organized her dinner party well and was quietly
singing to herself; she was in no great hurry. Sack retrieved
two tins of dog food from his supply in the pick-up, and after
I gave him his dinner he curled up for the night. He had
slimmed down, and was without the smell of skunk at last. I
suggested that we have a nice hot rum to give us an appetite
and a firm base to work on.

"I don't take rum," Minnie giggled. "But you fellows can."
I explained that a mink had eaten our butter, and I asked if
we could borrow a couple of ounces of oil for our drinks.

Slim exploded. "Don't put any of that stuff in mine!"

As Minnie was giggling something about eulachon oil
being better than either beaver or black-bear oil, a tired horse
with a rider clopped over the bridge. Old Joe. He rode to our
fire and dismounted.

"Been back in the hills."

"You stop for supper?" asked Minnie. "We got steak and
clams and oil."

"Gotta keep goin'. Got two riders bringing in some steers I
aint seen for two years. Don't know how they gottem. Wilder
than deer!"

I passed Joe a mug of rum.

"You got the best rum anybody," he said. "Got some taste!
What's wrong with that dog? Looks like he's dead."

"Just tired out."

"A shotta snoose'll perk him up. How was the river?"

"You were right, Joe. It's good going and there's plenty of
trout."

"Well, gotta go find a fresh horse and help get them steers
in."

Minnie's chowder was tasty and her biscuits were puffed
up like doughnuts. Then steaks and shaggy-mane mushrooms
sizzled from the pan. With no hint of fish. Her coffee was

delicious, and I like drinking unhurried mugs of fresh coffee with Minnie. She has about her a feeling of peace and an aura of calm as deep as a canyon pool.

"You take me to Nazko tomorrow?" she asked.

"Sure, but we'd like to catch some kokanee to take home."

"We move camp to that lil' lake tonight, and catch lotsa kickininees by sunup." White men are crazy. And every Indian knows it. But she would set her net and make me an accomplice.

"We'd like to catch them with our lines."

"Funny lil' fishes," nodded Minnie, very serious.

"Did you drive the pick-up here?" I asked.

"No-o," she giggled, "some boys from rancheree come by with Za-Louie. Bring it for you. I come 'long too. You see any girls ridin' up Chinee way?"

"You know, Minnie. It's impossible to keep secrets in this country."

"Not very big country, hey Bill."

No, not very big. Just a few thousand square miles and not many people in it. Maybe that's the secret.

"Long time ago, more people," said Minnie.

Chapter
Eighteen

The
Return

"I didn't say there was nothing better
. . . . I said there was nothing like *it."*

Through the Looking-Glass

Lewis Carroll

Our escape to the Blackwater was over. Like the old-time fur-traders who customarily shaved, bathed, and patched their clothes before proceeding to a main settlement, we scraped away the week's growth and dipped briefly in the river. We finished breakfast and then sorted our gear and loaded the pick-up. A small roadside lake provided us with some small fish to take home, while we mulled over the idea of simply moving to the woods and carving out our niches there. We agreed that perhaps the old fur-traders and Indians were not so crazy after all to choose isolation, but after dropping Minnie at the Rancheree, we visited Paul who decided to close up shop and go to Quesnel with us. We then decided that the time seems inevitably to come when the solitude seeker is defeated by his urban conditioning, or by his herd instinct.

When we'd left Slim and Paul, Sadsack and I headed for the office. The mail was stacked high. The secretary from the office next door wiggled in.

"Your boss is in town." A sweet tone, the tone of big sister advising little brother that father is going to give him a spanking. "Gosh, you look black!"

"I can't be too bad. I fell in a couple of times."

"I don't mean you're dirty, just tanned. You have no whiskers, but I still caught the sasquatch smell when you came up the hall. But I kind of like the smell of pine forest— and smoke."

"Maybe you'll surprise us all, and become a bush-bunny yet. What hotel is the boss camped in?"

"The usual, he said."

I phoned him, thinking that sometimes a good offensive is the best defensive.

"Hello, boss. I'm calling from the office."

"Well!" I heard. "Could you perhaps stay there a few minutes?"

"Sure, boss. Anything you say."

There was a screech of brakes in front of the building and I started opening mail. A bull in rut crashed the front door and charged down the hall.

"How long have you been away?" I thought I'd let him have his head and let him unwind.

"Where have you been? What have you been doing?" he continued.

"I went fishing."

"Fishing?!"

I wasn't doing very well. I told myself not to get excited, that there were other jobs, ones like checking life in sewer drains or flying aeroplanes. "Mad at me, boss?" A stupid question.

"Catch any? How big?"

"Ten pounds or so."

"On the fly?"

"On the fly."

"Ten-pounders. On the fly." A lowered tone. A reverent, wistful expression. A dreamy look.

"It isn't far out there," I said. "Of course, you haven't the time, and it's getting nippy at night. And the moose are

starting the rut and getting sort of mean, and you might have
to fork a horse for a way."

"Who hasn't the time? I'm due for a fishing trip!"

"I could clean up the office tonight," I said, but not very enthusiastically. "We could take off in the morning."

"To hell with the office! We'll do it when we get back."

I liked the "we" part.

"I'll go home and change."

"No! Go as you are. I'll drop a note to my office."

"The girl next door will knock it out."

Just as I returned from a discreet journey down the hall, he finished dictating, "hmmed" and "hawed" a couple of times, and added, "Please, would you mail these in four or five days?"

"I understand," the girl said dryly. I examined the ceiling.

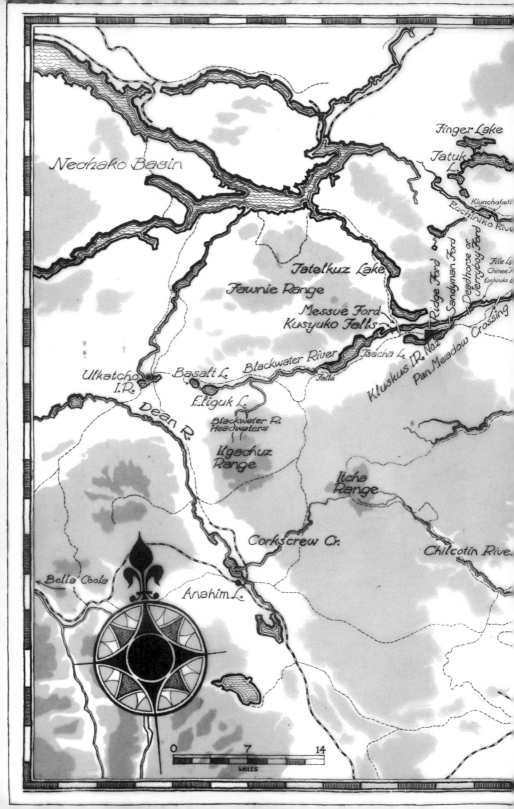